Violas of Britain and Ireland

BSBI Handbook No. 17

Violas of Britain and Ireland

BSBI Handbook No. 17

Michael Porter and Michael Foley

Illustrated by Sarah Holme

Edited by Christopher Boon

Botanical Society of Britain and Ireland
Bristol
2017

Published by the Botanical Society of Britain and Ireland
57 Walton Road
Shirehampon
Bristol
BS11 9TA

bsbi.org.uk

ISBN 978-0-90-115850-5

Designed by LTD Design Consultants
54 Warwick Square, London SW1V 2AJ
020 7931 7607, www.ltddesign.co.uk

Printed by Dolman Scott www.dolmanscott.com

BSBI is a company limited by guarantee in England and Wales (8553976) and a charity registered in England and Wales (1152954) and in Scotland (SC038675).

Contents

Preface and acknowledgements 2

Introduction 3

Characteristics and morphology 4

General *Viola* key 6

Illustrated key to violets (*Viola* sect. *Viola*) 9

Differences between similar pairs of *Viola* species 13

Species Accounts

1	*Viola odorata* L.	18
1 × 2	*Viola* × *scabra* F. Braun	26
2	*Viola hirta* L.	30
3	*Viola rupestris* F.W. Schmidt	36
3 × 4	*Viola* × *burnatii* Gremli	42
The *Viola riviniana* complex		44
4	*Viola riviniana* Rchb.	46
4 × 5	*Viola* × *bavarica* Schrank	54
4 × 6	*Viola* × *intersita* Beck	57
4 × 7	*Viola riviniana* Rchb. × *V. lactea* Sm.	59
5	*Viola reichenbachiana* Jord. ex Boreau	62
5 × 6	*Viola* × *mixta* A. Kern.	67
6	*Viola canina* L.	68
6 × 7	*Viola* × *militaris* Savouré	75
6 × 8	*Viola* × *ritschliana* W. Becker	78
7	*Viola lactea* Sm.	82
8	*Viola stagnina* Kit. ex Schult.	88
9	*Viola palustris* L.	94
10	*Viola cornuta* L.	100
11	*Viola lutea* Hudson	104
11 × 12	*Viola lutea* Huds. × *V. tricolor* L.	111
11 × 14	*Viola lutea* Huds. × *V. arvensis* Murray	116
12	*Viola tricolor* L.	118
12 × 14	*Viola* × *contempta* Jord.	126
13	*Viola* × *wittrockiana* Gams ex Kappert	128
14	*Viola arvensis* Murray	132
15	*Viola kitaibeliana* Schult.	136

Glossary 142

References and selected bibliography 144

Index 148

Preface and acknowledgements

This Handbook has been produced to help identification of Viola species and their hybrids. For a number of reasons it has been a long time in the writing. Early in the process, Clare O'Reilly who had originally taken on the project was compelled to withdraw due to pressure of work; we are grateful for her contributions and advice. Later, and for similar reasons, Paul Ashton had to resign as editor designate but, fortunately, Chris Boon was able to take over and, with calmness, efficiency and good humour, has guided the project to completion. We owe him a considerable debt of gratitude.

The plan was to use photographs of all the taxa described but we found the shortness of the Viola flowering season and the rarity of some of the hybrids created problems. Sometimes it was necessary to wait until the next season, or the following one to obtain the details and photographs that were needed. Despite our extensive use of photographs, we felt that line drawings of live material were essential to show the diagnostic points of each of the species. We were fortunate to obtain the services of Sarah Holme who was able to fit our requirements into a busy schedule of professional and family life. We are grateful for her expertise and attention to detail and feel that the results clearly express the character and individuality of each taxon. Distribution maps are an essential part of the BSBI series of handbooks and we are grateful to Stephanie Rourke (CEH) for preparing the latest versions of the maps and to David Pearman for organising and checking them.

We list below the many other people who have contributed in various ways to this Handbook, by sharing their knowledge of taxa, sites and ecology or by making constructive comments on the text. To all of them we offer our thanks and apologise to any we may have inadvertently omitted:

Andy Amphlett, Pat and Charles Baker, Christine Bartram (CGE), Alex Bateson, David Benham, Ian Bennallick, Ian Bonner, Margaret Bradshaw, Michael Braithwaite, Mike and Corinne Brindle, Helen Brown, Phill Brown, Peter Bullard, Arthur Chater, Julie Clarke, Rod Corner, Helena Crouch, Declan Doogue, Carl Farmer, Lynne Farrell, Christian Feuillet, Garden House Nurseries, Jane Gilmour, Paul Green, Ron Groom, Anne Haden, Geoffrey Halliday, Mike Hardman, David Hickson, Miles Hodgkiss, Roger Holme, Trevor James, Alan Johnson, Philippe Julve, Ann Kitchen, Mark and Clare Kitchen, Camilla Lambrick, Bob Leaney, Alan Leslie, Alex Lockton, Trevor Lowis, Jim McIntosh, Desmond Meikle, Tim Melling, Chris Miles, Tony Mundell, Dawn Nelson, Rachel Nicholson, Tony O'Mahony, Clare O'Reilly, Philip Oswald, Steve Parker, David Pearman, John Poland, Ted Pratt, Martin Rand, Mo Richards, Jeremy Roberts, Linda Robinson, Marie Saag, Janet Simkin, Mary Smith, Paul Smith, Roger Smith, Clive Stace, Pete Stroh, Geoff Toone, Jesse Tregale, Kevin Walker, Robin Walls, Jeanne Webb, Mike Wilcox, Colin Wild, Mike Wyse Jackson and Gordon Young.

Thanks are also due to the authorities at Lancaster University for providing Michael Foley with the support and facilities which have greatly helped him in carrying out the work on this project. Finally, Mike Porter would like to thank his wife, Julia, for her help and advice in the preparation of the text and for her patience and understanding during the years spent in the preparation of this handbook.

Introduction

Although some of the 200 plus species of *Viola* in the world are found in Australasia and in mountainous regions of South Africa and South America, they occur mainly in the more temperate areas of the Northern Hemisphere. Europe has more than 90 species and Britain and Ireland 13 with 2 additional subspecies. Several of these, notably *Viola riviniana*, occur over the length and breadth of these islands and *V. riviniana* itself is found from sea-level to well over 1,000 m. Others, such as *V. kitaibeliana*, *V. stagnina* and *V. rupestris*, occur in only a few closely circumscribed areas. A number of species, including *V. lactea*, *V. odorata* and *V. reichenbachiana,* favour the southern parts of Britain and Ireland but *V. lutea* is found in the more mountainous regions of Wales, northern England and Scotland and other species such as *V. canina* and *V. tricolor* are thinly scattered from the Channel Islands to the Orkneys. In other words, most areas have at least some species of *Viola* growing commonly in suitable habitats and many people must be familiar with the genus *Viola* even if they do not separate the plants they see into individual species – except into the broad division of violets and pansies and, perhaps, into that of scented and unscented flowers. Some of our native violets are also the main foodplants of several fritillary butterfly species and this is one of the many reasons why it is essential that *Viola* populations are not endangered. Small bouquets of the scented species especially were sold by urban street vendors in the Victorian era and even later.

In the less urban societies of the past violets must have been even more familiar and their frequent occurrence in literature is not surprising. Shakespeare speaks of 'violets dim, But sweeter than the lids of Juno's eyes Or Cytherea's breath' (The Winter's Tale), Keats of 'fast-fading violets covered up in leaves' (Ode to a Nightingale) and Milton of 'the violet-embroidered vale' (Comus). In the language of flowers, codified by the Victorians but centuries older, violets in general were considered to stand for modesty and faithfulness, although, in contrast, Geoffrey Grigson in *The Englishman's Flora* points out that *Viola odorata* Sweet Violet 'was the flower of Aphrodite and of her her son Priapus' and thus may be associated with sexual love (Grigson, 1955).

Similarly, it is not surprising that such a well-known flower should have been considered to have medicinal value. The Ancient Greeks, seeing it as a symbol of fertility, are said to have used it in love potions – and also as a calmative and to reduce anger. The Romans used it in a liniment to ease gout and, worn in a garland about the head, as a means of warding off headaches and dizziness. In later herbals different parts of the plant were recommended variously for application on wounds, as a treatment for insomnia, as a laxative and an emetic, as a remedy for bruises and a soothing drink for sore throats. The flowers are rich in vitamin C and provitamin A.

The attractiveness and aesthetic appeal of violets were widely recognised in the past leading to extensive cultivation experiments, including hybridisation, aimed at producing plants for horticultural use which were of even greater appeal. The brightly coloured, large-flowered pansies seen in today's gardens are largely a result of this.

The particular scent and flavour of violets have also been employed in the making of sweets such as 'Parma Violets', wines and alcoholic liqueurs and crystallised cake decorations, often known as candied violets. The flowers when fresh can also be added to salads or fruit cups to give extra flavour or colour.

Characteristics and morphology

British and Irish species of the genus *Viola* can be annual or perennial. Pansies (section *Melanium* Ging.) may be either annual or perennial while all violets (section *Viola*) are perennial. Some violets have creeping stolons (runners) or soboles (underground shoots) and form extensive patches. Other violets and all pansies lack stolons or soboles (although *V. lutea* has creeping rhizomes) and grow in small clumps. Their leaves are alternate, stalked, entire, with paired stipules (small leaf-like or scale-like structures) at the base. Their flowers are solitary, stalked, with paired bracteoles (tiny leaf-like structures) around the midpoint of the stalk. The flowers themselves are five-petalled (upper pair, lateral pair and spurred lowest petal) with five sepals at the base with sepal appendages (small flaps at the stem end of the sepal). They have five stamens with the style usually bent but sometimes straight. The seeds are held in three-valved capsules.

Chasmogamous (open) flowers, pollinated by insects, most commonly bees, are produced early in the season but, as daylight hours lengthen, production ceases and the chasmogamous flowers are replaced by cleistogamous flowers (small flowers without petals which do not open) which are self-pollinated. Both types of flower produce seeds, the cleistogamous ones rather more in number than the chasmogamous flowers. The seeds of some violets bear elaiosomes – fleshy substances rich in nutrients. Seed dispersal is ballistic, the seeds being ejected forcefully by the ripe capsule. However, this is often supplemented by dispersal by ants (myrmecochory) which are attracted to the seeds by the elaiosomes which they may eat on the spot or carry away to their nest. Although the elaiosomes are eaten, the seeds themselves are not and, while they may not be carried far from the parent plant, they are often relocated to a site where they are safer from predation and where nutrients are more readily available (Culver & Beattie, 1978).

Hybrids are not infrequent. They often attract attention by their vigour, the abundance of their flowers, the large size of the plants themselves or of their flowers or leaves. After flowering they usually fail to set seed and thus few or no capsules are formed. Dead, brown withered flowers which remain on the plant long after flowering are often a good indicator of the possibility of hybridity. However, this character alone is not conclusive proof and needs to be supported by evidence of intermediacy.

Viola leaves tend to get larger as the season progresses but this is especially noticeable with *V. hirta*, the hybrid *V. hirta* × *odorata* (*V.* × *scabra*), *V. reichenbachiana* and *V. palustris.*

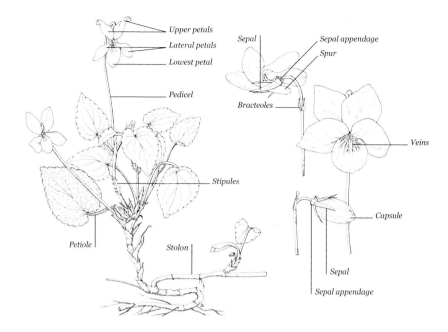

Viola taxa can be variable in their morphology. Thus, with all species and, especially, their hybrids identification should never be based on a single character. Wherever possible a suite of characters should be used. The characters most useful for identification are listed below:

Habit – the point on the plant from which the leaf- and flower-stalks arise.

Stolons – present or absent.

Petioles (leaf stalks) – hairy or not.

Stipules – length, shape (lobed or entire), edges toothed or fringed with glandular or fine-tipped hairs (fimbriate).

Leaves – overall shape, shape of apex, shape of base, hairy or not.

Pedicels (flower stalks) – hairy or not.

Bracteoles – position on pedicel.

Sepals – acute or blunt.

Sepal appendages – large or small.

Flowers – colour, veining on lowest petal (degree of branching), presence or not of tuft of hairs on lateral petals, shape of upper and lateral petals.

Spurs – size, colour, straight or curved upwards, notched or not.

Capsules – shape, hairy or not.

General *Viola* key

This key includes hybrids which, in a vegetative state, may be impossible to name with certainty. The tables for each of the hybrids, which are found in the main accounts section, may help to elucidate some problems. Further clues are given in the section 'Differences between similar species pairs' (p. 13) which, although not dealing specifically with hybrids, gives more details about the differences between their parents. Additionally, there may be different forms of the hybrid between the same two parents, closer to one or the other and not exactly intermediate between them.

1   Stipules lanceolate, entire to toothed, the teeth often tipped with hair-like points (fimbriate); flower stems solid _____ **VIOLETS** __ 2

1   Stipules deeply lobed but not toothed or fimbriate; flower stems hollow _____ **PANSIES** __ 17

2   Leaf and flower stalks arising directly from creeping underground rhizome, no leaf- or flower-stalks from above ground stems _____ **9 *V. palustris***

2   Leaf and flower stalks arising directly from base of plant or from above-ground stems _____ 3

3   Leaf and flower stalks arising directly from base of plant, no leafy stems; sepals blunt _____ 4

3   Plants with leafy flowering stems; sepals acute _____ 6

4   Stolons absent; plants in small clumps; petioles and leaves with dense, spreading hairs __ **2 *V. hirta***

4   Stolons present; plants forming patches; at least some hairs on petioles and leaves deflexed ____ 5

5   Petioles with dense, short, deflexed hairs only; leaves to 3.2 cm long at flowering time; capsules frequent _____ **1 *V. odorata***

5   Petioles with deflexed and/or short spreading hairs; leaves to 4.5 cm long at flowering time; flowers large, no or few capsules forming _____ **1 × 2 *V.* × *scabra***

6   Leafy flowering stems arising from around or below a rosette of leaves; leaves not or little longer than wide _____ 7

6   Leafy flowering stems arising from base of plant, no rosette of leaves; leaves longer than wide, sometimes twice as long as wide or more _____ 11

7   Leaves very small, usually no more than 1.5 cm in length; petioles often with short dense covering of hairs, sometimes glabrous, especially around Ingleborough _____ 8

7   Leaves larger, usually more than 1.5 cm in length; petioles glabrous or, very occasionally, with scattered long hairs _____ 9

8   Leaves with rounded apex; upper surface glabrous or with scattered very short hairs; capsules globular _____ **3 *V. rupestris***

8   Leaves with slightly pointed apex; upper surface with scattered long hairs and, often, short hairs near leaf margins; capsules absent _____ **3 × 4 *V.* × *burnatii***

9   Upper surface of leaves matt; soboles sometimes present; spurs usually paler than corolla, notched; sepal appendages > 1.5 mm _____ 10

9   Upper surface of leaves often slightly shiny; soboles always absent; spurs darker than corolla, not notched; sepal appendages < 1.5 mm _____ **5 V. reichenbachiana**

10   Upper petals narrow and usually not overlapping; veins on lowest petal little branched; capsules only rarely produced _____ **4 × 5 V. × bavarica**

10   Upper petals broad and overlapping; veins on lowest petal much branched; capsules frequent _____ **4 V. riviniana**

11   Leaves ± triangular in outline; corollas bluish-violet or, occasionally, violet _____ 12

11   At least some leaves considerably longer than broad; corollas almost white to pale violet or pale blue _____ 13

12   Plants forming small clumps; leaf bases truncate or shallowly cordate; upper leaf surface glabrous; corollas bluish violet _____ **6 V. canina**

12   Plants often forming large clumps or broad patches; leaf bases cordate; upper leaf surface with some long scattered hairs; large corollas ± violet in colour _____ **4 × 6 V. × intersita**

13   Leaves up to twice as long as broad (but often much less) _____ 14

13   Leaves 2 to 4 times as long as broad _____ 16

14   Leaves with truncate or cuneate bases (never cordate); upper surface glabrous _____ 15

14   Some leaves with cordate bases; scattered hairs on upper surface; corollas pale violet, not or rarely forming capsules _____ **4 × 7 V. riviniana × lactea**

15   Upper stipules large, sometimes as long as petiole; upper and lateral petals three times as long as broad; corollas pale greyish-violet; capsules frequent _____ **7 V. lactea**

15   Upper stipules small, less than half length of petiole; upper and lateral petals less than twice as long as broad; corollas pale with bluish tinge; capsules usually not forming ___ **6 × 7 V. × militaris**

16   Leaves 2 to 3 times as long as broad; corollas pale blue; capsules not or rarely forming _____ **6 × 8 V. × ritschliana**

16   Leaves 2 to 4 times as long as broad; corollas pale blue to almost white, often appearing round; capsules frequent _____ **8 V. stagnina**

17   Spurs 10-15 mm _____ **10 V. cornuta**

17   Spurs up to 7 mm _____ 18

18   Corollas 35-60 mm vertically; petals strongly overlapping _____ **13 V. × wittrockiana**

18   Corollas less than 35 mm vertically; petals not strongly overlapping _____ 19

19   Plant with long creeping rhizomes; habit compact; corollas relatively large, 20-35 mm vertically _____ **11 *V. lutea***

(Plants bearing smaller corollas than *V. lutea*, with white upper petals, the others yellow or tinged yellow, but with corollas larger and less cup-shaped than in *V. arvensis*, may represent the putative hybrid between the two species _____ **11 × 14 *V. lutea* × *arvensis*)**

19   Plant lacking rhizomes or, if present, very short; corollas < 22 mm _____ 20

20   Corollas usually 18-22 mm vertically; habit lax; petals blue often admixed with yellow, cream, and white, much longer than sepals _____ **12 *V. tricolor***

(Plants with lax habit but large (> 22 mm) corollas, in the north and west of Britain, should be checked for the possibility of the hybrid _____ **11 × 12 *V. lutea* × *tricolor*)**

20   Corollas usually < 18 mm vertically; petals cream-yellow sometimes tinged bluish, never longer than sepals (or much shorter) _____ 21

21   Upper petals +/- equalling sepals; corollas creamy in colour, often tinged blue _____ **12 × 14 *V.* × *contempta***

21   Upper petals variably shorter than sepals; corollas small, usually < 12 mm vertically _____ 22

22   Plant usually relatively large (to 40 cm tall), branched; corollas usually 8-12 mm vertically, petals much shorter than sepals _____ **14 *V. arvensis***

22   Plant usually very small (to 10 cm tall), with no or very few branches; corollas *c.* 5 mm vertically, upper petals slightly to much shorter than sepals _____ **15 *V. kitaibeliana***

The growth habit of violets can be extremely useful in deciding to which group of violets an individual plant belongs. There are four main types illustrated here:

Leaves and flowers arising directly from creeping rhizome (V. palustris).

Leaves and flowers arising directly from base of plant; no leafy flowering stems (V. hirta and V. odorata).

Flowers on leafy stems; no leaf rosette (V. canina, V. lactea and V. stagnina).

Leafy flowering stems arising from around a rosette of leaves (V. riviniana, V. reichenbachiana and V. rupestris).

NB the following key is not dichotomous.

1   Stipules ovate to lanceolate, entire to toothed, the teeth often tipped with hair-like points (fimbriate) ⎯⎯⎯⎯⎯⎯⎯⎯⎯⎯⎯⎯⎯⎯⎯⎯ **1 to 9 VIOLETS** ⎯ 2

1   Stipules leaf-like, deeply lobed but not toothed or fimbriate ⎯ **10 to 15 PANSIES** (See general key)

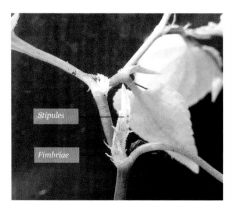 

Couplet 1: Violets (left) and pansies (right).

2   Leaves and flowers arising from creeping underground rhizome, no stems above ground ⎯⎯⎯ 3

2   Leaves and flowers arising direct from base of plant or from above-ground stems ⎯⎯⎯⎯ 4

3   Leaves long-stalked, kidney-shaped; flowers long-stalked pale violet; leaf stalks usually glabrous but sometimes hairy; in marshes mainly in the west of Britain and Ireland ⎯⎯⎯ **9 *V. palustris***

4   Leaves and flowers arising direct from base of plant, no leafy stems; sepals blunt ⎯⎯⎯⎯ 5

4   Plants with leafy flowering stems; sepals acute ⎯⎯⎯⎯⎯⎯⎯⎯⎯⎯⎯⎯⎯⎯⎯ 6

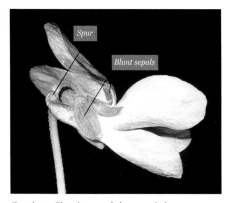 

Couplet 4: Showing sepal characteristic.

5   Leaf and flower stalks with dense, short, deflexed hairs; stolons present; flowers usually scented, dark violet (often white, occasionally other colours) _____ **1 *V. odorata***

5   Leaf and flower stalks with dense, spreading hairs; stolons absent; flowers unscented, pale blue-violet _____ **2 *V. hirta***

Couplet 5: Deflexed (left) and spreading (right) hairs on the petiole.

6   Leafy flowering stems arising from around or below a rosette of leaves; leaves little longer than wide _____ 7

6   Leafy flowering stems arising from base of plant, no rosette of leaves; leaves longer than wide, sometimes twice as long as wide _____ 8

7   Leaves ovate-orbicular with cordate bases and pointed apices, leaf and flower stalks (almost always) glabrous; corollas violet often with dark zone on lowest petal; spurs notched, usually paler than corolla (plants in exposed situations may be very small)_____ **4 *V. riviniana***

7   Leaves ovate-orbicular with cordate bases and often acuminate apices, leaf and flower stalks glabrous; corollas violet with a tinge of red, often with dark zone on lowest petal; spurs unnotched, usually darker than corolla _____ **5 *V. reichenbachiana***

7   Plants very small, leaves almost round with shallowly cordate base and raised edges (like scoop), leaf and flower stems sometimes covered with short, dense hairs (but often glabrous or nearly so around Ingleborough); corollas pale violet-blue (white at Arnside Knott), no dark zone on lowest petal; spurs short, pale, unnotched; very rare on limestone in northern England_____ **3 *V. rupestris***

Triplet 7: Showing flower characteristics.

8   Leaves ± triangular with truncate or shallowly cordate bases, becoming more lanceolate higher up the stem; corollas often but not always slatey-blue; spurs straight and (often strikingly) yellow, usually notched _____ **6 *V. canina***

8   Leaves lanceolate with cuneate or truncate bases (not cordate); corollas milky-violet; spurs short yellowish and unnotched; local in Wales, southern and western England and Ireland ____**7 *V. lactea***

8   Leaves ovate to lanceolate, 2 to 4 x as long as wide, with truncate to subcordate bases; corollas very pale blue or white with round petals; spurs very short and unnotched; an extremely rare plant of base-rich fens in Cambridgeshire and Oxfordshire and also rare in turloughs in Ireland_____
_____ **8 *V. stagnina***

Triplet 8: Leaf bases: Cordate (left), truncate (centre) and cuneate (right)

Key differences between similar pairs of *Viola* species are listed below. However, it should be borne in mind that Violets and Pansies can vary from the norm, particularly later in the season or when growing in atypical conditions. A number of examples of each character should be considered before coming to a conclusion with regard to that character and as many characters as possible before reaching a decision as to species. The possibility of hybridity should also be considered.

1 *Viola odorata* and 2 *Viola hirta*

1) *V. odorata* is strongly stoloniferous; *V. hirta* has no stolons.
2) The hairs on the petioles of *V. odorata* are deflexed or appressed; those of *V. hirta* are spreading and patent.
3) The petiole hairs of *V. odorata* are up to 0.4 mm in length; those of *V. hirta* are up to 0.6 mm in length. (The difference, though apparently slight, is readily distinguishable when the petioles are compared under a lens.)
4) The stipules of *V. odorata* are ovate-lanceolate; those of *V. hirta* are lanceolate.
5) The leaves of *V. odorata* are generally orbicular in shape and thus almost as broad as long and with a deeply cordate base; those of *V. hirta* are up to 1.6 times as long as broad and have a shallowly cordate or truncate base.
6) In *V. odorata* the bracteoles are usually below the midpoint of the pedicel; in *V. hirta* they are usually at or above the midpoint.
7) The sepal appendages of *V. odorata* are patent; those of *V. hirta* are appressed.
8) The corollas of *V. odorata* when violet have a deep, rich hue but are frequently white, occasionally pink or apricot and, very rarely, other colours; those of *V. hirta* are almost invariably some shade of violet.
9) *V. odorata* can be extremely fragrant, although some of the colour variants have no, little or an unpleasant scent; *V. hirta* has no scent.
10) *V. odorata* usually flowers distinctly earlier than *V. hirta*, the first flowers appearing in February, although var. *praecox* may come into flower in November or December; *V. hirta* usually comes into flower in March.

3 *Viola rupestris* and 4 *Viola riviniana*

Viola rupestris, an extremely rare violet in Britain, occurring in only four districts of northern England where it grows only on Carboniferous limestone, differs considerably from lowland or sheltered forms of *V. riviniana* and few problems should be found in distinguishing them. However, difficulties increase when trying to differentiate between *V. rupestris* and small upland forms of *V. riviniana* (sometimes but not always var. *minor*) which are the variants most likely to be found growing in proximity to *V. rupestris*. Difficulties, especially in the field, are exacerbated by the often extremely small size of both plants. A lens and patience are both essential but with care most specimens can be confidently named.

1) The petioles and pedicels of *V. rupestris* are often covered with a dense indumentum of short hairs, although, commonly in the Ingleborough area and occasionally elsewhere, they may be glabrous; the petioles and pedicels of *V. riviniana* are almost always glabrous.

2)   The stipules of *V. rupestris* are dentate and only slightly fimbriate; those of *V. riviniana* are distinctly fimbriate.
3)   The leaves of *V. rupestris* have raised edges at the sides but not at the base (giving the scoop shape); those of *V. riviniana* are raised only at the base and not at the sides (thus appearing flat).
4)   The leaves of *V. rupestris* are usually blunt-tipped; those of *V. riviniana* have a pointed tip.
5)   The upper surface of the leaves of *V. rupestris* usually appears glabrous but closer examination with a lens and bending the leaf over the finger will sometimes show a scattered covering of extremely short hairs or bristles (to .05 mm/50 μm), usually located towards the edges of the lobes; the same process applied to *V. riviniana* will show much longer hairs (to 0.33 mm/330 μm). (In both cases the hairs may be inconspicuous, especially in the case of *V. rupestris*.)
6)   The colour of the upper surface of the leaves of *V. rupestris* is a dark somewhat glossy green; that of *V. riviniana* is a lighter less glossy green.
7)   The corollas of *V. rupestris* are paler than those of *V. riviniana* best described as a 'pale blue- violet'; those of *V. riviniana* are best described as 'blue-violet'.
8)   The lowest petal of the corolla of *V. rupestris* has no zone of darker violet immediately below the white zone; many, but not all, flowers of *V. riviniana* possess this darker zone.
9)   The veins on the lowest petal of *V. rupestris* are not greatly branched; those of *V. riviniana* are usually much branched.
10) The spurs of *V. rupestris* are short, conical and unnotched; those of *V. riviniana* are stout and notched at the tip.
11) The capsules of *V. rupestris* are usually globose, slightly trigonous and with a blunt tip; those of *V. riviniana* are strongly trigonous, often pointed and larger.
12) The capsules of *V. rupestris* are sometimes covered with a dense indumentum of short hairs; those of *V. riviniana* are always glabrous.

4 *Viola riviniana* and 5 *Viola reichenbachiana*

1)   *V. riviniana* often produces soboles (underground stems); soboles are not found with *V. reichenbachiana*.
2)   The stipules of *V. riviniana* are broader and have shorter fimbriae than those of *V. reichenbachiana*.
3)   The leaves of *V. riviniana* are proportionately broader (1.4 times as long as wide) and generally have shorter and less acute tips than those of *V. reichenbachiana* (1.6 times as long as wide).
4)   The leaves of *V. riviniana* do not increase greatly in size at fruiting time; those of *V. reichenbachiana* often become considerably larger.
5)   The hairs on the upper surface of the leaves of *V. riviniana* occur over the whole surface; those of *V. reichenbachiana* tend to avoid the veins.
6)   In *V. riviniana* the sepal appendages are longer than 1.5 mm; those of *V. reichenbachiana* are smaller being less than 1.5 mm in length.
7)   The sepal appendages of *V. riviniana* increase in size after flowering; those of *V. reichenbachiana* remain the same size.
8)   The corollas of *V. riviniana* have a blue-violet colour (but never as blue as those of *V. canina*); those of *V. reichenbachiana* often have a very slight red tinge in their violet colour.
9)   The veins on the lowest petal of *V. riviniana* are usually much branched; those of *V. reichenbachiana* are unbranched or scarcely branched.

10) The upper petals of *V. riviniana* are broad and overlap; those of *V. reichenbachiana* are narrower and often twisted or folded back and more erect than those of *V. riviniana*, thus often giving the impression of 'rabbit's ears'.

11) The spurs of *V. riviniana* are paler than the corolla, usually rather whitish or yellowish in colour, broad, upcurved and notched on the top; those of *V. reichenbachiana* are usually darker than the corolla, often dark purple (although sometimes concolorous), and are narrow, straight and un-notched.

12) The capsules of *V. riviniana* usually contain about 20 light brown seeds; those of *V. reichenbachiana* 12 dark brown seeds.

13) *V. riviniana* flowers from March until May; *V. reichenbachiana* flowers appreciably earlier from February to the end of April, although there is a considerable period of overlap.

4 *Viola riviniana* and 6 *Viola canina*

1) *V. riviniana* has a non-flowering rosette of leaves at the top of the rootstock (not always easy to find); with *V. canina* all leaves are on flowering stems.

2) The stipules of *V. riviniana* have numerous, fimbriate, sideways pointing teeth; those of *V. canina* have few, short, usually forward-pointing teeth.

3) *V. riviniana* leaves are ovate-orbicular with a strongly cordate base; those of *V. canina* are roughly triangular in shape with a shallowly cordate or truncate base.

4) The leaves of *V. riviniana* are mid to bright green; those of *V. canina* are dark green and feel thicker in texture.

5) The upper surface of the leaves of *V. riviniana* often has many short patent hairs (use lens and bend leaf over finger to determine this character); the upper surface of the leaves of *V. canina* is glabrous or almost so.

6) The corollas of *V. riviniana* are violet in colour; those of *V. canina* are usually (but not always) bluer and lack the violet tinge of *V. riviniana*.

7) The lowest petal of *V. riviniana* very often has a dark zone immediately below the white patch in the throat; *V. canina* lacks this dark zone.

8) The spurs of *V. riviniana* are white, pale yellow or violet; those of *V. canina* are usually a deep, often very striking yellow.

4 *Viola riviniana* and 7 *Viola lactea*

While *V. riviniana* is widespread and often common throughout Britain and Ireland, *V. lactea* has a very restricted distribution, being found only along the western, southern and south-western coasts of England and Wales and in a few places along the Irish coast. In all other situations it can be safely discounted as a possibility.

1) *V. riviniana* has a central non-flowering rosette, although this may sometimes be hard to make out; *V. lactea* lacks this central non-flowering rosette.

2) The stipules of *V. riviniana* are toothed and fimbriate; those of *V. lactea* are longer but less toothed and fimbriate except towards the base.

3) The leaves of *V. riviniana* are ovate-orbicular; those of *V. lactea* are lanceolate or ovate-lanceolate.

4) The bases of the leaves of *V. riviniana* are cordate; those of *V. lactea* are truncate, cuneate or rounded.
5) The corollas of *V. riviniana* are a strong shade of violet; those of *V. lactea* are pale violet or almost white.
6) The lowest petal of *V. riviniana* often, though not invariably, possesses a dark zone below the white patch in the throat; that of *V. lactea* has no dark zone.
7) The spurs of *V. riviniana* are usually whitish, pale yellow or violet; those of *V. lactea* are yellowish or greenish.

6 *Viola canina* and 7 *Viola lactea*

1) The growth habit of *V. canina* is usually more compact than that of *V. lactea*.
2) The stipules of *V. canina* are short with a small number of short, forward-pointing teeth; those of *V. lactea* are longer (sometimes equalling the internode at the top of the stem) with fimbriate teeth near the base.
3) The leaves of *V. canina* are roughly triangular in shape with a truncate or shallowly cordate base; those of *V. lactea* are longer, lanceolate or ovate-lanceolate in shape and with a cuneate or decurrent (never cordate) base.
4) The leaves of *V. canina* are green below; those of *V. lactea* green often with a purplish tinge.
5) The corollas of *V. canina* usually have a bluish tinge; those of *V. lactea* are much paler, often almost white.
6) The upper petals of *V. canina* are obovate, usually one and a half times to twice as long as wide; those of *V. lactea* are narrower, up to three times as long as wide.

11 *Viola lutea* and 12 *Viola tricolor* subsp. *tricolor*

The absence of *V. lutea* from most parts of southern and eastern England and from much of Ireland, means that there is often no problem in deciding which of these two is in question.

1) *V. lutea* is usually a species of upland grassland and metalliferous areas, especially lead mines, up to 1,050 m above sea-level; *V. tricolor* is found in ruderal habitats, in wastelands, in arable fields and their margins and on sand dunes, usually at low levels and has never been recorded at more than 450 m.
2) *V. lutea* has long, creeping rhizomes; *V. tricolor* usually lacks rhizomes, but, if present, they are short and undeveloped.
3) *V. lutea* is a small plant with little branched or unbranched flowering stems with only one (or occasionally two) disproportionately large flowers per stem; *V. tricolor* has a laxer, more rambling habit and branched or much branched flowering stems with several flowers per stem.
4) The corollas of *V. lutea* measured vertically are 20-35 mm; those of *V. tricolor* are often distinctly smaller, measuring 18-22 mm. (This character should not be used alone, but only in conjunction with other characters, since, occasionally, *V. tricolor* can have larger flowers than *V. lutea*.)
5) The spurs of *V. lutea* may be up to three times as long as the sepal appendages; those of *V. tricolor* are no more than twice as long as the appendages.

When these two species grow together, as is often the case in arable fields, *V. arvensis* may exhibit a denser growth habit and be more leafy in the upper parts with comparatively short internodes. Hybrids between the two are frequent in such situations, are partially fertile and sometimes backcross. Consequently, it may be extremely difficult to determine the identity of plants without flowers.

NB Whilst *V. kitaibeliana* is only known from the Isles of Scilly and Channel Islands, it can occur there in ruderal habitats. There it is readily separated from the superficially similar *V. arvensis* by its much smaller flowers and petals, the corollas being *c.* 5 mm in height as opposed to *c.* 12 mm in the case of *V. arvensis*.

1) With *V. arvensis* the mid-lobe of the stipule is usually ovate or ovate-lanceolate, crenate-serrate and leaf-like; that of *V. tricolor* is lanceolate and entire, not appearing leaf-like.
2) With *V. arvensis* the arch of the pedicel is often distinctly grey-blue in colour; the pedicel arch of *V. tricolor* does not have this coloration.
3) The sepals of *V. arvensis* appreciably exceed the petals in length, sometimes being twice as long; those of *V. tricolor* are much shorter than the petals, sometimes only half the length.
4) *V. arvensis* has small corollas, rarely more than 12 mm measured vertically; those of *V. tricolor* are usually appreciably larger measuring 18-22 mm.
5) The corollas of *V. arvensis* are largely yellow and white; those of *V. tricolor* are largely blue but very often with a combination of purple, violet, yellow and cream. (Some *V. arvensis* flowers occasionally have tinges of violet which may be the result of introgression.)
6) The corollas of *V. arvensis* are often somewhat cup-shaped; those of *V. tricolor* are flat.

Sweet Violet

Viola odorata is characterised by its stoloniferous habit, its fragrance (not occurring, however, in all the varieties), its blunt-tipped sepals, its petioles clothed with deflexed hairs, its orbicular leaves with deeply cordate bases and its precocious flowering.

A perennial herb growing from a central point but with long stolons which root at the tip leading to the forming of large patches; leaf stems and pedicels arise from the base of the plant. **Petioles** clothed with short appressed, deflexed hairs, of variable density. **Stipules** pale green; long-triangular; fringed with short glandular hairs. **Leaves** orbicular or broadly ovate; often small, sometimes < 2.0 cm long as first flowers open, becoming larger at peak flowering time (2.0-)2.5-5.0(-9.0) cm in length, usually slightly longer than wide but sometimes wider than long, crenate; apex obtuse; base deeply cordate; clothed on both surfaces with short, patent, hairs and feeling soft to the touch; fresh green and shiny when newly unfurled; becoming darker and increasing in size later in the season and remaining around the plant, often in moribund form, throughout subsequent autumn and winter. **Pedicels** glabrous, sometimes with patent hairs above bend. **Bracteoles** at or above midpoint of pedicel. **Sepals** pale green, sometimes dotted with purple; blunt-tipped; fringed with patent hairs; appendages short, somewhat patent. **Flowers** usually fragrant but some varieties unscented;

V. odorata *showing the rich violet flowers and the shiny new leaves with an old leaf, bottom right (March).*

Viola odorata.

An extensive patch of V. odorata (var. dumetorum*) growing by the M6 motorway (Cumbria, March).*

often opening as new leaves are unfurling; usually violet or white, sometimes showing variations between the two colours, occasionally red-purple, pink or tinged with apricot; veins faint on white petals, darker on violet ones; lateral petals usually with tuft of hairs near inner tip (except in var. *imberbis* and var. *subcarnea*). **Spurs** sometimes hooked upwards, stout, purplish-green (but see varieties); exceeding sepal appendages; unnotched. **Capsules** round, up to 12 mm; densely covered with short patent hairs. Flowering February to late April (but see var. *praecox* which often begins flowering in November). **Chromosome number** 2n = 20.

V. odorata is widespread but thins out to the north and the west. Although there is some doubt about its status, it is generally considered to be largely native as far north as Westmorland and Durham; in Ireland only plants occurring in the south-east are considered to be native. However, there may be native populations outside these areas and there are certainly introduced populations within them, sometimes containing the less common varieties. The widespread purple-flowered var. *odorata*, also known as var. *typica*, is considered to be mostly native with other colour forms often being introductions and rarely occurring far from habitation. However, the white-flowered var. *dumetorum* occurs in natural situations and may in places be more frequent than the purple form, especially in areas on the edges of the range of *V. odorata*. It is thought that this variety could possibly be native in Cornwall. *V. odorata* occurs commonly throughout mainland Europe except in the extreme north, in both the east and west of the USA and in eastern Australia. Additionally, there are populations in Mexico, South America, New Zealand and Japan.

V. odorata is usually a plant of fertile, base-rich, often calcareous, moist soils, but with a wide tolerance of light or shade. It is most commonly found in lightly shaded situations but can thrive in the open, often perhaps protected to one side by a hedgerow or other vegetation, and also in the shade of sparse woodland. It frequently occurs on roadside banks or hedgerows and also in scrub, open woodland, on woodland margins and sometimes in plantations. It seems often to do well in churchyards where it may have been introduced by man, and in other semi-natural situations such as roadsides close to habitation and parks. It is a lowland species and has not been recorded at altitudes above 190 m, which, in Kershope Forest, north Cumbria, is its greatest known altitude.

V. odorata *showing side view of corolla with blunt-tipped sepals, small, patent sepal appendages and hooked spur.*

The conservation status in Britain is Least Concern (Cheffings & Farrell, 2005) and is the same in England (Stroh *et al.*, 2014) and, provisionally, in Ireland (M.B. Wyse Jackson, pers. comm., 2015). Because many plants of *V. odorata* are naturalised, escapes or introductions, it is very difficult to judge whether its distribution is increasing or declining. In most parts of Britain and Ireland numbers appear to be stable or increasing, though how many of the plants concerned are truly native is a matter of conjecture.

V. odorata is present in NVC community **W8** *Fraxinus excelsior-Acer campestre-Mercurialis perennis* woodland (Rodwell, 1991-2000).

Common associates include *Alliaria petiolata, Allium ursinum, Anemone nemorosa, Anthriscus sylvestris, Arum maculatum, Conopodium majus, Ficaria verna, Fragaria vesca, Fraxinus excelsior, Geum rivale, Glechoma hederacea, Hedera helix, Hypericum perforatum, Melica uniflora, Mercurialis perennis, Myrrhis odorata* (especially in northern England), *Potentilla sterilis, Primula vulgaris, Stellaria neglecta, Urtica dioica, Vicia sepium* and *Viola hirta* (on wood edges on calcareous soil).

The orbicular seed capsule of V. odorata *densely covered with patent hairs. Note also the patent sepal appendages.*

Probably the earliest reference made to *V. odorata* is that by Thomas Johnson as '*Viola purpurea*' between Gravesend and Rochester in Kent (v.c. 16 W. Kent) (Johnson, 1629). In 1666, Christopher Merrett gave what is presumably the first record of the white colour form (var. *dumetorum*) as being found by Dr Gunthorp in Cornwall (v.c. 1a W. Cornwall or v.c. 2 E. Cornwall): '*Viola martia alba odoratissima*' (Merrett, 1666).

A tuft of stipules of V. odorata *below unfurling leaves in early spring.*

V. odorata *showing the short, deflexed hairs on the petioles.*

A detached stipule of V. odorata *showing the long-triangular shape and the short glandular fimbriae.*

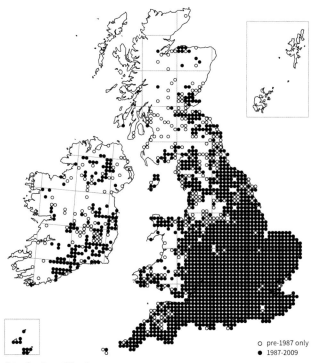

○ pre-1987 only
● 1987-2009

Distribution of V. odorata.

Notes

Fragrance – As is the case with many sweetly-scented flowers, the ambient temperature plays a significant role. Flowers collected on a cool day may have little apparent fragrance but once brought into the warmth of a house their fragrance may fill the room. This is indeed the case with *Viola odorata* which, being in flower very early in the year, often has to contend with frost by night and cold winds by day. Nevertheless, on a mild sunny early spring day the scent of a massed bank of Sweet Violets can be very strong and almost overpowering close to. It is claimed, however, that the scent, though so strong at first, can be very fleeting and appears to be lost almost immediately. This is said to be because one of the constituents is ionine which has the power to deaden or anaesthetize the receptors in the nose thus, for a while, making the scent undetectable. However, this does not always appear to be the case, small-scale practical experiments suggesting that, for some people at least, the fragrance remains constant.

Flowering – *V. odorata* is the earliest of the *Viola* species to come into flower, often in February, at which time the previous season's long-stalked leaves are still present, often in an untidy moribund form, around the base of the plant. Occasionally, a small number of chasmogamous flowers are produced in August and September.

Infraspecific taxa and hybrids

- var. *odorata* (or var. *typica)*
- var. *dumetorum* (Jord.) Boreau
- var. *imberbis* (Leight.) Hensl.
- var. *praecox* Greg.
- var. *subcarnea* (Jord.) Parl.
- var. *sulfurea* (Cariot) Rouy & Foucaud
- an unnamed variety with white petals and a white spur
- forma *lilacina* Rossm.
- hybridises with *V. hirta* (*V.* × *scabra*) (see **1 × 2**)

Over the years many varieties of *V. odorata* have been named, largely on the basis of corolla colour which can range from different shades of violet, through pink and orange to white. Some, if not all, of these different colour forms are considered to be introductions and it may be that only the traditional violet coloured forms are genuine native plants. However, one white variety (var. *dumetorum*) occurs widely, as mentioned above, particularly on the edges of *V. odorata*'s range, where it may be the most common variety (as in north Cumbria and Cornwall). Other colour forms are very much scarcer and often occur on roadsides and near habitation, nearly always in the southern half of Britain. In several cases the varieties are much less hairy than *V. odorata* var. *odorata*. Additionally, the fragrance of some varieties is often much less strong than that of the typical variety and may even, sometimes, be distinctly unpleasant (described variously as smelling rather rank with overtones of silage, dung or BO).

Some of the recognised varieties or forms are described and pictured below but intermediates are also widespread.

V. odorata var. odorata (or var. *typica*) – flowers with a deep violet corolla and spur, variable in shade and ranging from blue-violet to a rather redder tone; lateral petals with tuft of hairs towards inner end.

V. odorata var. dumetorum – flowers with white corolla with almost invisible veins and dark spur, usually violet or purple; lateral petals with tuft of hairs towards inner end.

V. odorata var. imberbis – flowers with pure white (occasionally violet) corolla and pinkish-purple spur, paler in colour than that of var. *dumetorum*; lateral petals lacking the tuft of hairs towards the inner end. Found in the southern half of Britain on chalk and limestone.

V. odorata *var*. odorata.

V. odorata *var*. dumetorum.

V. odorata *var*. imberbis.

V. odorata *var*. praecox.

V. odorata var. praecox – flowers and whole plant usually smaller than var. *odorata*; leaves almost orbicular; flowers with deep violet-purple (sometimes almost black) corolla and spur; lateral petals with or without tuft of hairs towards inner end; usually starting to flower in November or even earlier in some years and continuing until March or April. The flowers do not appear to open fully and capsules are rarely formed. Found mainly in the south-west of Britain.

V. odorata* var. *subcarnea – flowers dusky (or muddy) pink with violet spur; lateral petals usually lacking tuft of hairs and thus sometimes considered simply to be a pink form of var. *imberbis*. Found in the southern half of Britain on chalk and limestone (the same range as var. *imberbis*).

V. odorata* var. *sulfurea – flowers with centre of corolla apricot, becoming paler towards edges, spur pinkish-purple; flowers often more open than in other varieties; lateral petals usually with tuft of hairs.

V. odorata *var. subcarnea*.
Photo: A.R.G. Mundell.

V. odorata *var.* sulfurea.

V. odorata *var.* sulfurea.

V. odorata *var.* 'leucoium'.

***V. odorata* var.** – flowers white or occasionally the palest blue, lateral petals with tuft of hairs, spur white, occasionally slightly greenish. This variety is officially unnamed, although A.C. Leslie (pers. comm.) has suggested the name var. *leucoium*.

V. odorata* f. *lilacina – flowers with white corolla more or less overlaid with pale mauve or lilac but very variable; spur darker, solid purple; lateral petals with tuft of hairs; often found where dark and white violets occur together and not usually given varietal status. Often very strongly scented.

V. odorata *f.* lilacina.

***V. odorata* reddish forms** – There are a number of forms of *V. odorata* which have a distinct reddish tinge to the corolla colour, sometimes approaching the red of the continental *V. odorata* f. *rubriflora*. Such plants occur almost wholly in the south of England and may have large or small flowers and be early or late flowering. The strength and nature of their fragrance is very variable.

V. odorata *reddish form*.
Photo: T.J. James.

V. × scabra *showing the large flowers, the white centre to the corolla and the large leaves.*

Viola odorata × *V. hirta*

Viola × *scabra* is a variable, largely sterile (about 90%) hybrid, initially distinguished from its parents by its particularly vigorous growth habit, its abundant, large flowers, often on long pedicels (a character particularly noticeable early in the season) and its large leaves (usually noticeably larger than those of either parent), which become even larger later in the season, measuring up to 9 × 7 cm with petioles sometimes more than 20 cm long. It resembles *V. odorata* in forming extensive spreading patches (resulting from the presence of stolons) and in the soft texture of its leaves. It is closer to *V. hirta* in the colour of its flowers, which tend to lack the deep, rich hues of *V. odorata*. Also, the flowers have a white centre to the corolla, are almost unscented and have denser, more patent hairs on the petioles. However, variants exist which are closer to each of the parents, some of which may be strongly scented. We know of no hybrids involving the other colour varieties of *V. odorata*, although Gregory describes a plant which she considered to be a hybrid between *V. odorata* var. *subcarnea* and *V. hirta* (Gregory, 1912).

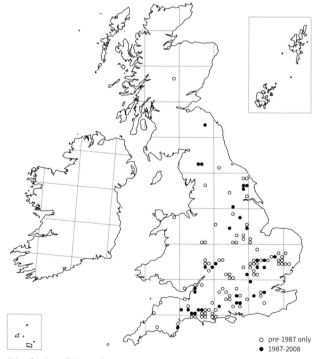

○ pre-1987 only
● 1987-2008

Distribution of V. × scabra

26

V. × scabra, *showing a vigorous, floriferous patch, densely packed with flowers, resulting from its stoloniferous habit – end of March.*

A closer view of the same patch two months later showing the large leaves of V. × scabra *totally dominating the hedge-bank with their dense growth and size – late May.*

V. × scabra is widely but thinly scattered in England, very rare in Scotland and Wales and apparently absent from Ireland, although it seems likely that it is much under-recorded. It occurs in western and central mainland Europe north to Scandinavia and is to be expected wherever the species meet.

Above: Flower of V. × scabra *showing the white centre to the corolla. Melkinthorpe, Cumbria.*

Below: Site for V. × scabra. *Grassy bank on chalk hills, Dunstable Downs, Bedfordshire. Photo: C.R. Boon.*

V. × *scabra* is usually found in thin woodland and along woodland edges, in open scrub on the slopes of calcareous downs and escarpments and on roadside banks and track sides, often in the company of both parents but sometimes with one only. Like *V. odorata*, it is a lowland plant.

Note

Nomenclature – At one time, plants closer to *V. odorata* were given the name *V.* × *sepincola* and those closer to *V. hirta* the name of *V.* × *permixta* (Gregory, 1912) and were sometimes considered to be full species.

Close-up of petiole of V. × scabra *showing both patent and deflexed hairs.*

Viola odorata	*Viola* × *scabra*	*Viola hirta*
Forms large, spreading, untidy patches.	Forms large, spreading patches, usually taller than either parent.	Usually forms neat, compact clumps.
Stolons present.	Stolons present.	Stolons absent.
Petiole hairs appressed 0.4 mm long.	Petiole hairs patent/deflexed variably intermediate in length.	Petiole hairs patent, 0.6 mm long.
Stipules ovate.	Stipules triangular.	Stipules lanceolate.
Leaves (at flowering) 3 × 3 cm; surfaces with short hairs, feeling soft.	Leaves (at mid-flowering) large *c.* 4.5 × 4 cm; surfaces with short hairs, feeling soft; leaves (later in season) very large 9 × 7 cm.	Leaves (at mid-flowering) *c.* 3.5 × 2.4 cm; surfaces with sparse short hairs, not feeling soft.
Bracteoles above midpoint of pedicel.	Bracteoles below midpoint of pedicel.	Bracteoles below midpoint of pedicel.
Sepal appendages patent.	Sepal appendages intermediate.	Sepal appendages appressed.
Corollas to 2.2 cm vertically; dark violet or white (occasionally pink or apricot).	Corollas to 2.5 cm vertically; white centre to corolla; closer in colour to those of *V. hirta*.	Corollas to 2.3 cm vertically; pale violet blue.

Hairy Violet

Viola hirta is characterised by its tufted habit, its lack of stolons, the spreading hairs on its petioles and the underside of its leaves, its blunt sepals and its blue-violet, unscented flowers.

A perennial herb growing from a central tuft and lacking stolons; leaf stems and pedicels, arising from the base of the plant, up to *c.* 35 cm high, but usually much less. **Petioles** usually densely covered with long, patent hairs. **Stipules** pale; lanceolate; fimbriae often tipped with glands. **Leaves** ovate, 1.0-4.5(-9.0) cm long (1.0-2.0 cm long in var. *calcarea*), *c.* 1.5 × as long as broad, rather shiny on upper surface, crenate; apex obtuse to subacute; base shallowly cordate, occasionally truncate; patent hairs on both surfaces of leaf (particularly obvious when furled early in the season); becoming considerably larger as the season progresses. **Pedicels** ± glabrous or with variable quantities of patent or deflexed hairs. **Bracteoles** usually well below midpoint of pedicel. **Sepals** purplish; blunt with fringe of short straight hairs; appendages small and appressed. **Flowers** unscented; appearing before the leaves are fully unfurled; whitish before opening, becoming blue-violet; corolla very variable from *c.* 1.5-2.3 cm, measured vertically; lateral petals usually with tuft of hairs near inner tip; veins on lowest petal often inconspicuous, not or little branched. **Spurs**

Clump of V. hirta, *late March, Cumbria.*

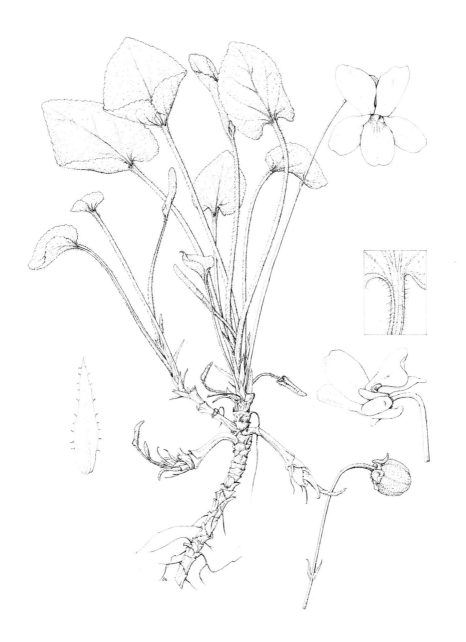

Viola hirta.

Corolla of V. hirta *showing the inconspicuous, little branched veins.*

The blunt sepals of V. hirta *with appressed appendages and purplish spur.*

slightly hooked, to 4.0 mm; greenish, dotted purple; up to 2 × as long as sepal appendages; unnotched. **Capsules** round, to 10 mm; pubescent. **Flowering** (late) March to April or (early) May. **Chromosome number** 2n = 20.

V. hirta reaches its northern limits in Kincardineshire in the east and Dumfriesshire in the west. It is widespread in England, being most common in central southern England and the south Midlands and occurring as far south as western Cornwall and the Isles of Scilly. It is absent from much of the north Midlands, the northern part of East Anglia and mid-Wales. It is rare in Ireland, occurring only in three discrete areas: Co. Dublin and Co. Kildare in the east, Co. Clare and Co. Limerick in the west and on the Aran Islands. *V. hirta* is widespread in mainland Europe from the southern parts of Scandinavia to Spain and Italy and eastwards to the Caucasus and Siberia.

V. hirta is normally found on dry to slightly damp calcareous soils. It usually occurs in short vegetation in open or slightly shaded situations, such as downland and limestone grassland, and, in suitable areas, is often common on roadsides and railway embankments. However, it also grows in thin scrub or on rides or woodland edges. In limestone districts it occurs on rocky slopes and limestone pavements. Although often thought of as a lowland species, it is common, for instance, on the limestone hills of Westmorland and has been recorded from over 600 m (on limestone) on Long Fell in the northern Pennines. Along the coast it may be found in sand dunes. It has also been recorded from more acidic sites where these are flushed with base-rich water.

The patent hairs on the petiole of V. hirta, *one character which distinguishes this species from* V. odorata. *Note the lanceolate stipules (left) with gland-tipped fimbriae.*

The conservation status in Britain is Least Concern (Cheffings & Farrell, 2005) and is the same in England (Stroh *et al.*, 2014). In Ireland it is provisionally classified as 'Near Threatened at least, Vulnerable likely' (M.B. Wyse Jackson, pers. comm., 2015). It is not known to occur in Northern Ireland (Preston *et al.*, 2002). Although not under serious threat in Britain, *V. hirta* has lost ground throughout its range due to agricultural improvements and loss of habitat. In Ireland it appears to have been lost from a number of sites, often as a result of quarrying and overgrazing.

NVC communities in which *V. hirta* occurs include **CG1** *Festuca ovina-Carlina vulgaris* grassland, **CG2** *Festuca ovina-Avenula pratensis* grassland, **CG3** *Bromus erectus* grassland, **CG4** *Brachypodium pinnatum* grassland, **CG5** *Bromus erectus-Brachypodium pinnatum* grassland, **CG6** *Avenula pubescens* grassland, **CG7** *Festuca ovina-Hieracium pilosella-Thymus praecox/pulegioides* grassland, **CG8** *Sesleria albicans-Scabiosa columbaria* grassland and **CG9** *Sesleria albicans-Galium sterneri* grassland (Rodwell, 1991-2000).

Frequently associated species include *Achillea millefolium, Brachypodium sylvaticum, Carex caryophyllea, C. flacca, Dactylis glomerata, Festuca ovina, Galium sterneri, Helianthemum nummularium, Hypericum perforatum, Neottia ovata, Poterium sanguisorba, Primula*

Separate clumps of V. hirta *growing on an open sunny slope in Cumbria, early April.*

veris, *P. vulgaris*, *Sesleria caerulea* (on Carboniferous limestones of northern England), *Thymus praecox*, *Viola odorata* (on woodland edges and under thin tree or scrub cover) and *V. riviniana*. It sometimes grows in distinguished company with such associates as *Anacamptis morio*, *Aquilegia vulgaris*, *Carex ericetorum* and *Viola rupestris*.

V. hirta was first recorded in Kent (v.c. 15 E. Kent) by Christopher Merrett as '*Viola fol. Trachelii serotina hirsuta ad radice lignosa*' in 'Charlton Wood and in the lane leading to Sittingbourn' (Merrett, 1666).

Notes

Aberrant flowers – All plants can throw out aberrant forms from time to time but *V. hirta* flowers seem particularly susceptible to producing unusual numbers of spurs. These can vary from 2 to 4 or there may be no spur at all or a highly misshapen one, sometimes all flowers on a plant being affected, sometimes only one or two (Mundell, 2013). Possible reasons for this aberration have been suggested, including vibration and fumes from passing traffic since all sites reported by

Aberrant V. hirta *flower with four spurs. Photo: M. Hodgkiss.*

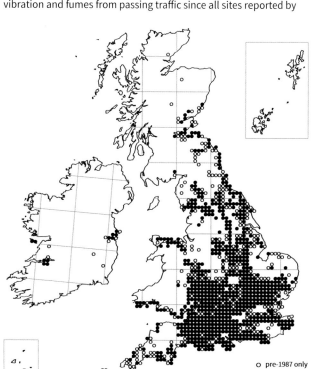

○ pre-1987 only
● 1987-2010

Distribution of V. hirta.

34

Mundell were from roadsides or areas subject to heavy use while none were from totally undisturbed areas (M. Hodgkiss, pers. comm.).

Insect food plant – *V. hirta* is one of the main larval food plants of two butterflies – the High Brown *Argynnis adippe* and the Dark Green Fritillaries *A. aglaja*. Both of these species have declined in recent years but the decline of the High Brown is more marked and a cause of serious concern with a 90% loss since the 1970s.

Infraspecific taxa and hybrids

- var. *calcarea* Bab. (formerly subsp. *calcarea* (Bab.) E.F. Warb.)
- hybridises with *V. odorata* (*V. × scabra*) (see **1 × 2**).

Viola hirta var. *calcarea* Bab.

This variant of *V. hirta* was at one time thought to be a separate species and was known as *V. calcarea* (Bab.) Greg. It was later reduced to subspecific status but is now considered by Stace (2010), whose conclusions are based on the work of Valentine and Moore, to be simply a variety. It has also been suggested that var. *calcarea*, with its impoverished flowers and generally later flowering period, may simply be a semi-cleistogamous form of *V. hirta* (Lousley, 1950).

V. hirta *var.* calcarea, *late April 2009.*

It is a smaller, usually later-flowering plant with flowers only up to 1.0 cm in size, with narrower, sometimes deeper coloured petals, the upper four often described as forming the shape of a St. Andrew's cross, and a shorter, straight spur, which may be equalled by the sepal appendages. Gregory (1912) describes the spur as 'almost imperceptible'. Specimens examined appear to be less hairy than normal *V. hirta*. At maturity the leaves, which rarely exceed 2.0 cm, are often folded upwards about the midrib. Var. *calcarea* occurs in open calcareous grassland, especially chalk downs, growing with normal *V. hirta* with which it is linked by a series of intermediates.

Spurs of V. hirta var. calcarea, *short and straight (left), and* V. hirta, *longer and hooked (right).*

Its distribution has not been mapped but it seems to be more common in the south of the range of *V. hirta* and there appear to be no records north of Yorkshire.

Teesdale Violet

Viola rupestris is characterised by its small size, by its round, scoop-shaped leaves, when flowering by its pale violet-blue flowers (white on Arnside Knott) which have no dark zone and by the short, dense indumentum on the petioles and pedicels (not always present in the Ingleborough and Long Fell areas).

A small or very small perennial herb with a vertical rhizome and a terminal non-flowering leaf rosette (the rosette leaves scarcely differing in size from the stem leaves and often not easy to make out); leafy, flower-bearing shoots arise from around the rosette to a height of 10 cm but usually very much less, often forming a tight cushion; stolons and soboles are not present. **Petioles** clothed in dense short indumentum, except, commonly in the Ingleborough area and occasionally on Long Fell, they may be much less hairy or entirely glabrous. **Stipules** usually lanceolate; with only a small number of teeth, these usually towards base only; short fimbriae sometimes present. **Leaves** ovate-orbicular, usually 0.75-1.2 cm long, up to 1.4 × as long as wide, crenate; sides raised to give characteristic scoop shape; dark green in colour; apex blunt; base widely cordate; sometimes glabrous but often with sparse, very inconspicuous extremely short, white bristles (to 0.05 mm) on basal lobes and along margins of upper surface. **Pedicels** covered with variable quantities of very short bristly hairs or glabrous. **Bracteoles** high on the pedicel,

The flower of V. rupestris *is rather paler in colour than that of the closely related* V. riviniana *and lacks the dark zone on the lower petal. The veins on the lowest petal are also less branched than in that species. Photo: T. Melling.*

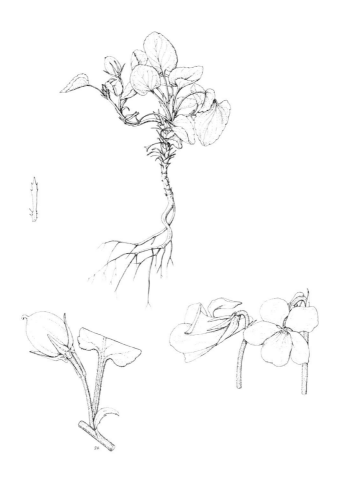

Viola rupestris.

The white form of V. rupestris *on Arnside Knott showing the scoop-shaped leaves and the dense indumentum on the flower stem. Photo: T. Melling.*

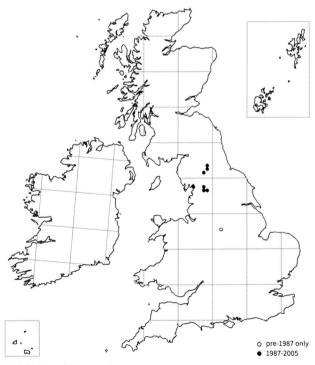

○ pre-1987 only
● 1987-2005

Distribution of V. rupestris.

just below bend; narrowly lanceolate. **Sepals** lanceolate; appendages short, rather square. **Flowers** unscented; varying in colour from 'a delicate pinkish-mauve' (M.E. Bradshaw in Jonsell *et al.*, 2000) to pale blue-violet, except at Arnside Knott where they are white; corollas to 2.0 cm high; upper and lateral petals ovate; lateral petals bearded; lowest petal lacking darker zone; veins with few branches. **Spurs** short, conical; paler than corolla; without groove. **Capsules** round and slightly trigonous, < 10 mm in length; glabrous or with indumentum of short stiff hairs; containing *c*. 10 seeds. **Flowering** late April to May (March to April at Arnside Knott). **Chromosome number** 2n = 20.

V. rupestris is known only in the north of England, in Cumbria, Yorkshire and Co. Durham, but it could still be found in other parts of northern England or Scotland where suitable habitat exists. Elsewhere, *V. rupestris* subsp. *rupestris* occurs in northern, eastern and central mainland Europe, the Caucasus, central Asia and Siberia. *V. rupestris* subsp. *relicta* is confined to the Scandes mountains of Norway, Sweden and Finland.

V. rupestris is a plant of open base-rich sites. In its *locus classicus* on Widdybank Fell it occurs on eroding sugar limestone, often in damp situations. On Long Fell and around Ingleborough it is found on limestone gravel, especially favouring sites by or in tracks or in hollows on limestone pavements, in cracks in low mounds of limestone bedrock, and sometimes in gaps in sparser *Sesleria*-dominated turf. On Arnside Knott it grows in semi-open limestone grassland in turf consisting largely of *Festuca ovina* and *Sesleria caerulea*. The altitude of the four sites ranges from 150 m (Arnside Knott) to 620 m (Long Fell).

Close-up of leaf of V. rupestris *showing scoop shape, blunt tip and dense indumentum on the petiole – Crummackdale, near Ingleborough.*

The Red Data status of *V. rupestris* is listed in Wigginton (1999) as being Near Threatened. However, in Cheffings & Farrell (2005) and in Stroh *et al.* (2014) its status is given as Least Concern, because, although it is known to occur in only four areas of England, some of the colonies are very extensive with large numbers of plants and the population as a whole is not in serious decline. Indeed, at three of its sites *V. rupestris* seems to be under no undue threat, the fear of its being 'hybridised out' (with *V. riviniana*) being exaggerated, but at Arnside Knott it has suffered from trampling and erosion due to the proximity of its site to a footpath. At this same site the strong growth of *Sesleria* due to the absence

V. rupestris *at its* locus classicus, *Widdybank Fell, Teesdale. Photo: F.J. Roberts.*

of adequate grazing has also had a detrimental effect. Remedial measures appear to have stabilised the population, although *Sesleria* remains a low-level potential threat. At Widdybank Fell the extreme fragility of its habitat has led to the loss of at least one site through erosion. This threat remains. At its classic site in Upper Teesdale about a tenth of *V. rupestris* habitat was destroyed in the construction of the Cow Green Reservoir between 1967 and 1971. *V. rupestris* is not known to occur in Ireland.

V. rupestris is present in the NVC community **CG9** *Sesleria albicans-Galium sterneri* grassland (Rodwell, 1991-2000).

Associated species include *Campanula rotundifolia, Carex caryophyllea, C. ericetorum, C. flacca, Danthonia decumbens, Festuca ovina, Lotus corniculatus, Pilosella officinarum, Pimpinella saxifraga, Sesleria caerulea, Thymus polytrichus* and *Viola riviniana.*

The first record (as *Viola arenaria* DC) appears to be that of the James Backhouses (father and son) in 1861 in Durham (v.c. 66 Co. Durham) 'at the upper end of Teesdale on the north side of the river' (Babington, 1863).

Notes

Flowering – At all sites *V. rupestris* is a very shy flowerer, sometimes less than 1% of plants producing chasmogamous flowers. These scarce chasmogamous flowers are usually produced rather later than those of most other *Viola* species, probably due to the high and exposed terrain of the sites (to 620 m on Long Fell), appearing usually at the end of April and during May. At Arnside Knott however, the site, at 150 m, is at a considerably lower altitude and subject to gentler climatic

The round, slightly trigonous, capsules of V. rupestris *in autumn. Photo: F.J. Roberts.*

40

conditions. Here the plants may well be in flower from early March onwards. Even more than in most *Viola* species, the later-appearing cleistogamous flowers seem to produce most of the capsules and the seeds, often producing the only fruits on plants that had been totally devoid of chasmogamous flowers.

Infraspecific taxa and hybrids

• hybridises with *V. riviniana* (*V.* × *burnatii*) (see **3** × **4**)

Molecular and morphological work carried out by Norwegian botanists (Nordal & Jonsell, 1998; Jonsell *et al.*, 2000; Nordal *et al.* 2005; Jonsell & Karlsson, 2010.) following earlier work by Jalas (1950), has confirmed that *Viola rupestris* occurs as subsp. *rupestris* and subsp. *relicta* Jalas. Two varieties of subsp. *rupestris* are also recognised: var. *rupestris* which is finely and evenly hairy, and var. *glaberrima* Murb. which is totally glabrous.

Subsp. *rupestris*, which is by far the more widespread, is generally a lowland plant and occurs on sand, gravel or limestone substrates. Plants are morphologically heterogeneous, being extremely variable as regards hairiness (some populations have plants which are totally glabrous), flower size and colour and leaf size.

Subsp. *relicta* populations occur in mountainous areas, solely on limestone substrates. They are morphologically homogenous, showing little variation in key characters. Plants have shorter hairs than those of subsp. *rupestris* but are never glabrous; they are also usually smaller with more truncate leaf bases.

Our plants do not fit comfortably with any of the above subspecies or varieties. The four populations all occur on limestone substrates of which three are in upland areas. In the Ingleborough area many plants are glabrous and plants from all four populations appear to be smaller than typical plants of subspp. *rupestris* and *relicta*, particularly in terms of leaf size and stem height. The length of the indumentum of the English plants is consistently shorter than that in either subspecies with a mean indumentum length of 0.05 mm, as opposed to the 0.15 mm of subsp. *relicta* and the 0.2 mm of subsp. *rupestris* (F.J. Roberts, pers. comm.). The English populations of *V. rupestris* may thus be referable to subsp. *rupestris*, subsp. *relicta* or possibly to an, as yet, undescribed subspecies. They may even comprise two subspecies since they differ considerably from each other. Judgement must be reserved until further work has been carried out. See Nordal *et al.* (2005) for further information.

Viola rupestris × V. riviniana

Viola × *burnatii* is a sterile, vigorous hybrid, sometimes forming large clonal patches, and is generally intermediate between the two parents. It is best identified at the end of the flowering season, in August or September, when the absence of capsules and the presence of withered aborted flowers in the leaf axils are good initial pointers to hybridity. These characters must, however, be confirmed by others: the intermediate shape of the leaves (more pointed at the apex than *V. rupestris* but less so than *V. riviniana* and lacking the strongly cordate base of *V. riviniana*) and, crucially, the combination of short hairs on the petiole and the pedicel (from *V. rupestris*) and longer hairs on the upper surface of the leaf (from *V. riviniana*), although these characters may be lacking in plants with a glabrous *V. rupestris* parent.

The hybrid between the white *V. rupestris* on Arnside Knott and *V. riviniana* is, perhaps surprisingly, as dark in colour as the hybrids at the three other sites in Britain where *V. rupestris* is pale blue-violet.

V. × burnatii *on Widdybank Fell.*

A single leaf of V. × burnatii *with an almost truncate base and blunt apex. Note also the aborted flower in the leaf axil and the stipule, bottom centre. Photo: F. J. Roberts.*

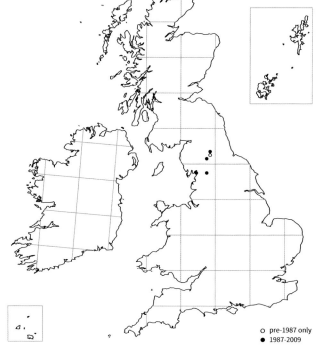

○ pre-1987 only
● 1987-2009

Distribution of V. × burnatii.

Viola rupestris	Viola × burnatii	Viola riviniana
Soboles absent.	Soboles sometimes present.	Soboles often present.
Leaf and flower stalks densely covered with short hairs (or glabrous).	Leaf and flower stalks densely covered with short hairs (or glabrous).	Leaf and flower stalks almost always glabrous.
Stipules toothed towards base, sometimes with short fimbriae.	Stipules toothed, sometimes with short fimbriae.	Stipules toothed and with long fimbriae.
Leaves truncate to slightly cordate at base; apex rounded.	Leaves truncate or moderately cordate at base; apex blunt.	Leaves deeply cordate at base; apex obtuse to pointed.
Leaves glabrous or with scattered very short hairs on upper surface, usually located near lobe edges.	Leaves with long hairs on the upper surface and (sometimes) very short hairs near lobe edges.	Leaves with relatively long hairs on upper surface.
Corollas pale blue-violet; dark zone absent.	Corollas pale blue-violet; dark zone very faint or absent.	Corollas blue-violet; dark zone usually present.
Capsules globular or very slightly trigonous.	Capsules absent; withered, remains of aborted flowers present.	Capsules trigonous.

V. × *burnatii* is of limited occurrence in Britain due to the extreme rarity of the *V. rupestris* parent. However, in all the four areas where *V. rupestris* occurs, its hybrid with *V. riviniana* has been found, sometimes in good quantities. Because of the altitude and exposure of most *V. rupestris* sites, small forms of *V. riviniana* (sometimes var. *minor*) are often involved. It is also recorded from western and central mainland Europe, north to Sweden (Stace *et al.*, 2015).

V. × *burnatii* is found only on base-rich limestone sites at altitudes of between 140 and 620 m, in the same general habitats as *V. rupestris*. However, in Jonsell *et al.* (2000) reference is made to its preference for deeper soils and its tolerance of denser turf than that parent.

Note

Conservation status – In Britain the conservation status of *V. burnatii* is Vulnerable and is the only *Viola* hybrid mentioned in Cheffings & Farrell (2005). It is not known to occur in Ireland.

The corolla of a V. × burnatii *plant from Widdybank Fell. Note the absence of dark zone on the lowest petal.*

The *Viola riviana* complex

As most botanists will acknowledge, difficulties can arise in distinguishing *Viola riviniana* from *V. reichenbachiana*. Although many specimens give no problems, there are numerous plants which appear to share key floral characters of both species, *viz.* flowers with the broader, overlapping petals and the much branched veins of *V. riviniana* but with the dark, unnotched spurs of *V. reichenbachiana* or flowers with the narrow petals of *V. reichenbachiana* but the pale, notched spur of *V. riviniana*. Sometimes such plants appear fertile with at least some full capsules while others fail to develop capsules of any sort, the dead flowers remaining on the plant for many weeks. The latter are obviously good candidates for the hybrid between the two species but fertile or partially fertile plants with a mixture of parental characters are much more difficult to name.

The general assumption has been that in Britain and Ireland the F1 hybrid between *V. riviniana* and *V. reichenbachiana* is largely sterile (Stace, 1975, 2010) and that there is little evidence for the existence of an F2 generation. However, work in continental Europe and especially in Germany (O'Reilly in Stace *et al.*, 2015) has demonstrated mean pollen fertility of up to 60% in the hybrid (Trees-Frick, 1993) and the existence of F2 and subsequent generations (Neuffer *et al.* 1999). This opens the way to the possibility of backcrossing and introgression which, if they occur over a prolonged period of time, could offer an explanation for those fertile specimens which appear to fit with neither *V. riviniana* nor *V. reichenbachiana*. If a similar situation obtains in Britain and Ireland, some of the puzzling fertile specimens we see today may result from historic introgression. Indeed, historic introgression of the two species in Britain and Ireland has been suggested by Valentine (1956) and Partridge (2007) and by other workers elsewhere in Europe, e.g. Schmidt (1961), Marcussen *et al.* (2001) and Harmaja (2003). The dark-spurred, later flowering plant sometimes known as *V. riviniana* var. *nemorosa* which occurs in shady woodland in various parts of Europe, including Britain and Ireland, seems to be a possible example of this. Determining such specimens poses problems, particularly in the field, even more so as there can no longer be confidence that hybrids will always be sterile.

Following field and herbarium work, C. O'Reilly (pers. comm.) has suggested a practical approach which, although in some ways controversial, seems to us to be a valuable contribution to the resolution of this problem, at least for field workers. This is to define both *V. reichenbachiana* and *V. riviniana* narrowly on grounds of morphology and ecology as we have done in the species accounts, and to regard all puzzling intermediate plants, not conclusively the hybrid, as part of the variation within the '*Viola riviniana* complex'. We think that this may be a useful approach but have also tried to give more 'traditional' ways of distinguishing these difficult forms. However, field botanists in particular will be aware that the traditional approach may not always lead to a definite or satisfactory determination of a given plant and that the best conclusion currently available may be that the plant is part of the '*Viola riviniana* complex'. Further work needs to be undertaken on the taxonomy of this group.

Common Dog-violet

Viola riviniana is very variable, but is usually easily characterised by its violet-coloured, broad, overlapping petals, the much branched veins on the lowest petal, the lanceolate sepals and the pale-coloured, notched spur.

A perennial herb with a vertical rhizome and a terminal non-flowering rosette of leaves (on some plants this rosette is difficult to make out); the rosette leaves are smaller but similar in proportions to the stem leaves; leafy, flower-bearing shoots arise from around the rosette to a height of 20 cm but often less, occasionally forming a rounded cushion; stolons are not present but underground stems (soboles) springing from adventitious buds on the roots often occur. **Petioles** usually glabrous. **Stipules** narrow (but broader than those of *V. reichenbachiana*); fringed with coarse fimbriae (distinctly shorter than those of *V. reichenbachiana*). **Leaves** ovate to broadly ovate, sometimes ovate-orbicular, (0.75-)1.5-3.5(-5.0) cm long, up to 1.4 × as long as wide, crenate; mid-green in colour; apex obtuse to somewhat

V. riviniana *showing the dark zone immediately below the white patch on the lowest petal, best seen in the flower on the left and absent in the flower on the right. Photo: J.R. Crellin.*

Viola riviniana.

acute; base cordate, basal lobes often slightly raised; usually with long, sparse inconspicuous white hairs on upper surface, some of which may run along the veins; increasing a little in size during summer but not as noticeably as those of *V. reichenbachiana*. **Pedicels** usually glabrous. **Bracteoles** below bend of pedicel; narrow-lanceolate; often reddish in colour. **Sepals** green often with darker central stripe; lanceolate, pointed; appendages large and square-cut, often notched or scalloped, > 1.5 mm in length; increasing in size as fruit matures. **Flowers** unscented; generally blue-violet but variable, occasionally all white; corolla to 2.5 cm high, pale in bud; upper and lateral petals obovate and overlapping; lateral petals bearded; lowest petal with long, much branched veins and often a zone of darker colour below the white patch in the throat. **Spurs** usually paler than corolla; blunt, stout; notched at tip. **Capsules** trigonous, obtuse to pointed, *c*. 10 mm in length; glabrous; containing about 18 light-brown seeds. **Flowering** March to May, occasionally again in August/September. **Chromosome number** 2n = 40.

V. riviniana *flower, showing pale, notched spur, overlapping upper petals and branched veins. The dark zone is not obvious on this flower.*

Viola riviniana is by far the most widespread and frequent of violets in Britain and Ireland, being found from the Isles of Scilly north to the Shetlands, from Co. Cork east to Norfolk and from lowland areas to high mountain summits. It is found on the Channel Islands and, in mainland Europe, from southern Italy to northern Scandinavia and from northern Spain east to Greece and western Russia. Outside Europe it also occurs in the Atlas Mountains of North Africa.

Viola riviniana appears largely indifferent to soil type, although it avoids wet and highly acid areas. It is extremely catholic in its habitat preference being found in open deciduous woodland or woodland glades, on wood edges, on hedge banks, on roadsides, in meadows, in mountain grassland (sometimes as var. *minor*), on moorland and on cliff ledges, ascending to a height of over 1,000 m in Perthshire, Scotland (v.c. 88 Mid Perth). *Flora Nordica* reports its existence in shady, mossy woodland, where, however, it does not flower (Jonsell & Karlsson, 2010). It appears able to thrive in apparently unsuitable conditions such as the thin soil of roadsides on the very edge of the tarmac while varieties such as var. *rosea* and var. *purpurea* may occur in the cracks between paving stones or between paths and house-walls.

Leaf of V. riviniana *showing rather sparse white hairs, often only seen by observing the leaf with a lens.*

The conservation status in Britain is Least Concern (Cheffings & Farrell, 2005) and is the same in England (Stroh *et al.*, 2014) and, provisionally, in Ireland (M.B. Wyse Jackson, pers. comm., 2015). Preston *et al.* (2002) report no decline in numbers and there appears to be no threat to its existence in Britain or Ireland.

V. riviniana occurs in many NVC communities: woodlands and scrub **W7-11**, **W14**, **W17**, **W19-24** and **W25**; mesotrophic grasslands **G2** and **MG3**; calcicolous grasslands **CG8-14**; calcifugous grasslands **U4**, **U5**, **U10**, **U13**, **U15-17**, **U19**, and **U20**; mires **M11** and **M38**; heaths **H6-8**, **H10-12**, **H15**, **H16**, **H18** and **H21**; shingle, strandline and sand-dune communities **SD8**, **SD9**, **SD12**, **SD14**, and **SD16**; maritime cliff communities **MC9**, **MC10** and **MC12**; vegetation of open habitats **OV38**. (Rodwell, 1991-2000).

Capsule of V. riviniana.

Among the many associated species are: *Ajuga reptans, Anemone nemorosa, Arum maculatum, Brachypodium sylvaticum, Conopodium major, Ficaria verna, Fragaria vesca, Glechoma hederacea, Hedera helix, Plantago lanceolata, Poa trivialis, Potentilla sterilis, Primula vulgaris, Vicia sepium, Viola canina* (in sand-dune and lake-side communities), *V. reichenbachiana* (in woodland over calcareous soils) and *V. rupestris* (in upland limestone grassland).

V. riviniana *showing pale spur, reddish bracteole, lanceolate, pointed sepals and large sepal appendages.*

V. riviniana *showing stipules fringed with fimbriae.*

Under 'wilde field Violet' Gerard (1597) may have been referring to *V. riviniana* when describing plants growing in Kent (v.c. 16 W. Kent) 'neere unto Blackeheath by Greenwich, at Eltham parke, with flowers of a bright reddish purple colour', although the colour seems unusual. Thomas Johnson mentions plants, also growing in Kent (v.c. 15 E. Kent) 'in woods near to Feversham' which may have been *V. riviniana* (Johnson, 1632).

Notes

Variability – *V. riviniana* is a very variable taxon, even more so than any other violet species. This may be because of its ability to thrive in a wide range of habitats and soil types. Some of the complexities are discussed in the section on the *Viola riviniana* complex (p. 44).

Hairiness – Apart from the sparse hairs found on the upper surface of the leaf *V. riviniana* is generally glabrous. However, occasional plants are found with scattered longish hairs on the petiole and, very rarely, the whole plant may be densely hairy. Such plants have been given the name of forma *villosa* but it is unclear whether this hairiness is retained

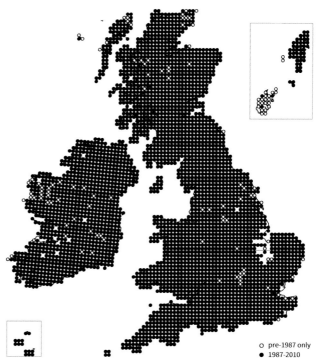

○ pre-1987 only
● 1987-2010

Distribution of V. riviniana.

when the plants are moved to a different habitat or indeed if offspring of hairy parents retain this character or revert to the normal glabrous state.

Flowering – *V. riviniana* usually comes into flower in mid-March, although a mild winter or early spring will advance the flowering time. After the first abundant flush of flowers, flowering often continues at a lesser intensity until May. Occasional chasmogamous flowers may occur later in the year in August or September. *V. riviniana* var. *minor*, growing in a more exposed habitat, tends to come into flower later.

Insect food plant – *V. riviniana* is of critical importance for several of the most attractive of British butterflies, among them species in serious decline. It is the main larval food plant of the High Brown Fritillary *Argynnis adippe* and one of the larval food plants of the Dark Green Fritillary *A. aglaja*, the Silver-washed Fritillary *A. paphia*, the Pearl-bordered Fritillary *Boloria euphrosyne* and the Small Pearl-bordered Fritillary *B. selene*.

Infraspecific taxa and hybrids

- var. *minor* (Murb. ex Greg.) Valentine
- hybridises with *V. rupestris* (*V.* × *burnatii*) (see **3** × **4**)
- hybridises with *V. reichenbachiana* (*V.* × *bavarica*) (see **4** × **5**)
- hybridises with *V. canina* (*V.* × *intersita*) (see **4** × **6**)
- hybridises with *V. lactea* (see **4** × **7**)

V. riviniana is a variable species which in the past has been split into a number of subspecies, varieties and forms (see *V. riviniana* complex, p. 44). We have followed Stace (2010) in rejecting all these except var. *minor*.

Variation seems to occur most frequently in later season plants growing in sheltered woodland habitats where the flowers may take on some of the characteristics of *V. reichenbachiana*, e.g. narrower, more separated upper petals and narrower, darker, sometimes mottled spurs. Such flowers may also, occasionally, have the slightly reddish hue of *V. reichenbachiana*. They are best distinguished from the latter by their later flowering, more branched veining on the lowest petal, rounder, less acutely tipped leaves and larger sepal appendages. (However, see the note on introgression in the *V. riviniana* complex section (p. 44).) Often, because of a more sheltered habitat and richer soil these plants may be larger than normal *V. riviniana*. They appear to be fully fertile.

Viola riviniana* var. *minor (Murb. ex Greg.) Valentine

This ecotype of exposed situations is smaller in all its parts than normal *V. riviniana* with leaves from less than 1 cm and the corolla up to 1.5 cm. The petals, especially the upper ones, appear to be proportionately narrower than in *V. riviniana* s.s. and scarcely

V. riviniana *var.* minor *growing in limestone grassland at 330 m near Caldbeck, Cumbria.*

overlap. However, var. *minor* is linked to the species by a series of intermediates and there are many plants which may be impossible to name precisely as to variety. Additionally, as with the species, leaves increase somewhat in size as the season progresses. Experimental work in the greenhouse (Valentine, 1941) has shown that var. *minor* retains its small stature when cultivated in less inhospitable situations. In this it differs from other small variants of *V. riviniana* which revert to normal size when taken into cultivation.

Cultivated taxa

There are a number of other varieties or forms of *V. riviniana* which have probably arisen spontaneously but which, because of their attractive appearance, have been taken into cultivation and are often found in or near gardens. All three of these varieties, together with variegated forms, may escape from gardens and occur on roadsides. The following three are probably the most popular and widespread.

Viola riviniana* f. *luxurians – A pure white variety, often with a greenish spur, sometimes, as here, with exceptionally large sepal appendages;

Viola riviniana *f.* luxurians.

apparently able to thrive in shade. The flower is just opening in the photograph.

Viola riviniana *var. Purpurea group.*

***Viola riviniana* var. Purpurea group**. Plants with deep violet flowers and purple-suffused leaves; often wrongly sold as *V. labradorica*. Extremely vigorous, tending to seed abundantly round about the parent plant.

Viola riviniana* var. *rosea – A pink variety often sold under the name of *V. arenaria* f. *rosea* or *V. rupestris rosea*. This is an extremely vigorous variety that can become invasive.

Viola riviniana *var.* rosea.

Viola riviniana × *V. reichenbachiana*

The hybrid between *Viola reichenbachiana* and *V. riviniana* is vigorous and floriferous and often comes into flower early in the season, roughly at the same time as *V. reichenbachiana* but continues to produce flowers until much later than that parent and indeed later than *V. riviniana*. It sometimes produces a second flush of variably sized chasmogamous flowers in July/August or even later (in November and December in the mild autumn of 2015). It is largely, although, importantly, not totally sterile with dead, shrivelled flowers often remaining on the plant until autumn or even until the following spring. Because of its variability and the difficulty of distinguishing it from one or the other parent, it is probably much under-recorded, particularly as it is said to occur wherever the parents cohabit (Valentine, 1975). Probably the best initial indicators of this hybrid are plants which hold their flowers later than either *V. riviniana* or *V. reichenbachiana* and/ or plants which have dead brown flowers which are not producing

A form of V. × bavarica *gathered in the wild and grown on in garden. 11 April 2011. The plant has soboles and is very vigorous and floriferous.*

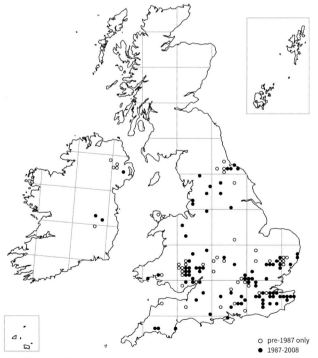

○ pre-1987 only
● 1987-2008

Distribution of V. × bavarica.

capsules. Hybrids will also show a mix of characters from both putative parents.

Records of *V. × bavarica* are thinly scattered throughout England, Ireland and Wales, its occurrences being tied to the somewhat restricted distribution of *V. reichenbachiana*. It has not been recorded in Scotland where the latter is very rare. It occurs throughout temperate Europe as far north as southern Sweden.

Like *V. reichenbachiana*, it is most often found on base-rich soils in woods and hedges over chalk and limestone.

Note

The table is based on one variant of the hybrid which has been closely observed over a number of years. There are, however, other variants which differ in detail, some being closer to *V. riviniana*, some to *V. reichenbachiana*, see, for example, Partridge (2007) who describes hybrids with **dark** notched spurs.

V. × bavarica *with dying flowers which remain on the plant for weeks or months and produce very few capsules.*

Flowers of Viola × bavarica, *from the same plant, showing characters from both parents: slight reddish tinge in corolla colour (*V. reichenbachiana*), well separated, rather narrow upper petals (*V. reichenbachiana*), little-branched veins on lowest petal (*V. reichenbachiana*), large sepal appendages (*V. riviniana*), spur (left hand plant) slightly paler than corolla (*V. riviniana*), (right hand plant) dark (*V. reichenbachiana*) but notched (*V. riviniana*). The photo on the left was taken in early April, that on the right on 1st November 2015 following a very mild early autumn. Another flower appeared in December.*

Viola riviniana	Viola × bavarica	Viola reichenbachiana
Often forms larger clumps or cushions.	Forms dense, floriferous patches.	Forms small clumps.
Often possesses soboles.	Sometimes has soboles.	Never has soboles.
Spurs whitish, notched.	Spurs same colour as, or paler than, the corolla, sometimes darker, notched.	Spurs dark, unnotched.
Corollas broad (c. 20 mm wide); lower petals overlapping, upper petals upright, overlapping; violet.	Corollas intermediate in size; usually lacking the twisted or folded back upper petals; closer to V. reichenbachiana in colour.	Corollas narrower (c. 17 mm wide); lower petals separated, upper petals twisted or folded back; violet with a tinge of red.
Veins on lowest petal much branched.	Veins on lowest petal intermediately branched; often only the two outer veins being branched.	Veins on lowest petal not or little branched.
Sepal appendages > 1.5 mm, increasing in size at fruiting.	Sepal appendages > 1.5 mm, usually increasing in size at fruiting (if this occurs).	Sepal appendages < 1.5 mm, not increasing in size at fruiting.
Leaves roughly 1.4 × as long as wide, increasing slightly in size at fruiting, apices obtuse to ± acute.	Leaf proportions and apices closer to those of V. reichenbachiana; leaves increasing in size but not greatly later in season.	Leaves roughly 1.6 × as long as wide, some greatly increasing in size at fruiting; apices more acute than those of V. riviniana.
Capsules containing c. 18 seeds.	Very few capsules with very few fertile seeds (but not fully sterile).	Capsules containing c. 12 seeds.

Viola riviniana × *V. canina*

Viola × intersita is a very vigorous, highly sterile hybrid often forming, by the soboles inherited from *V. riviniana*, broad floriferous patches or impressive clumps and coming into flower at the same time as, or a little earlier than, *V. canina* and thus rather later than *V. riviniana*. The abundant large flowers are slightly bluer in tone than those of *V. riviniana* but capsules do not form and brown, dead flowers remain on the plant long after flowering has finished. The two parent species often grow in close association and their attractive hybrid is one of the more widespread of violet hybrids of Britain and Ireland. Interestingly, *V. × intersita* has been noted in inland grassland sites in Roxburghshire where the *V. canina* parent is no longer present (Corner, 1989). Although many examples of this hybrid are large, striking plants there are instances when hybrids may be close to one or the other parent, differing only in minor characters from that parent.

Large clump of V. × intersita *in the dunes near Mawbray, Cumbria, May 2011.*

An extensive patch of V. × intersita *in disturbed sand dunes.*

A plant of V. × intersita *at the end of May, showing the dead flowers which fail to form capsules and remain on the plant.*

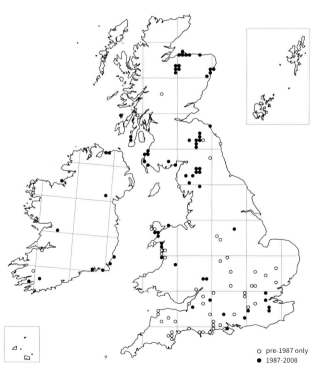

○ pre-1987 only
● 1987-2008

Distribution of V. intersita.

Viola canina	Viola × intersita	Viola riviniana
Plants forming small, loose clumps.	Plants often forming exceptionally large clumps or extensive patches.	Plants forming small, often neat, clumps.
Stipules lacking fimbriae.	Closer to *V. canina* but with some short fimbriae.	Stipules fimbriate.
All leaves on flowering stems (no terminal rosette).	All leaves on flowering stems (but sometimes one or two leaves inherited from terminal rosette of *V. riviniana*).	Non-flowering terminal rosette.
Leaves dark green, thick in texture	Leaves dark green, rather thick in texture	Leaves mid-green, not thick in texture.
Upper surface of leaves almost glabrous.	Upper surface of leaves with very sparse hairs.	Upper surface of leaves with sparse hairs.
Leaf bases truncate or shallowly cordate.	Leaf bases more cordate than in *V. canina.*	Leaf bases cordate.
Corollas to about 22 mm across.	Corollas somewhat larger (> 22 mm) than those of parents.	Corollas to about 22 mm across.
Lowest petal lacking dark zone.	Lowest petal sometimes with hint of dark zone.	Lowest petal often has clearly marked dark zone.
Spurs (sometimes bright) yellow.	Spurs intermediate; pale yellow.	Spurs usually white or pale.
Trigonous capsules forming.	No capsules forming.	Trigonous capsules forming.
Flower petals falling.	Dead flower petals remaining, sometimes for months, after flowering has finished.	Flower petals falling.

Flower of V. × intersita *showing large (more than 22 mm across), showy corolla and the absence of the dark zone below the throat.*

V. × intersita occurs throughout Britain and Ireland, although only occasionally, and in certain very limited areas such as the sand dunes of northern Cumbria and the shores of Derwent Water, may it be described as common. In such areas it may, by its vigour, constitute a threat to the existence of *V. canina*. It is widespread in mainland Europe, occurring as far north as northern Scandinavia.

V. × intersita occurs in open sites, often on acidic substrates. It is known from coastal sand dunes, inland sandy areas, stony river and lake shores and acid heathlands.

Viola riviniana × *V. lactea* is a largely sterile hybrid which is not uncommon in the sites where the parents cohabit. It is usually a vigorous, sometimes somewhat straggly, plant, variably intermediate between its parents in flower colour and in leaf shape. The most obvious diagnostic characters are the long leaves with truncate or slightly cordate bases, the variably pale violet corollas (sometimes violet with paler patches) and the dead brown flowers which remain on the plant. Closer examination often reveals different kinds of leaves on the same plant; the long leaves with cuneate or truncate bases inherited from *V. lactea* and, closer to the ground, the shorter more cordate leaves inherited from *V. riviniana*. *V. riviniana* × *lactea* often forms large clumps, spreading by means of the soboles also inherited from *V. riviniana*.

In Britain and Ireland this hybrid occurs, or has occurred, in almost all areas where *V. lactea* is found and there are particular concentrations in Cornwall, the New Forest and Anglesey. In some sites its vigorous

V. riviniana × lactea *showing the long, somewhat intermediate leaves, the violet corollas with paler patches and the dead flowers which remain on the plant without forming capsules. Photo: K.J. Walker.*

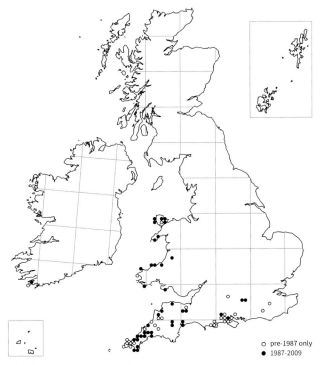

○ pre-1987 only
● 1987-2009

Distribution of V. riviniana × lactea.

V. riviniana × lactea *showing the pale violet of the corolla colour and the absence of a dark zone.*

The two types of leaves often found in V. riviniana × lactea*: to the left and at the top the longer leaves with truncate or cuneate bases inherited from* V. lactea*; to the right and at the bottom the shorter leaves with more cordate bases inherited from* V. riviniana*. There are also some intermediate leaves. (Plant grown on in garden.)*

growth may lead to its outcompeting both its parents, as on stretches of the Cornish coast (French *et al.*, 1999). Because of the limited distribution of *V. lactea* in mainland Europe this hybrid appears to be known only from France and Portugal.

Like its *V. lactea* parent, this hybrid is found mainly on dry heaths, often on the edge of gorse or bramble thickets, occasionally on the tops of sea-cliffs. It is often quick to colonise burnt or disturbed ground.

V. riviniana × lactea *showing the pale yellow spur and the obvious sepal appendages.*

V. riviniana × lactea *showing stipules much more fimbriate than in* V. lactea.

Viola riviniana	Viola riviniana × lactea	Viola lactea
Central non-flowering rosette.	Loose, vigorous, rather straggly growth habit often with a small number of cordate leaves suggesting central rosette.	No central rosette.
Stipules shorter than those of *V. lactea*; bearing more numerous, fimbriate teeth.	Stipules intermediate; more teeth than *V. lactea*, some of them with fimbriate tips.	Stipules long, lanceolate; with very few short teeth.
Leaves ovate-orbicular, deeply cordate at base.	Stem leaves variably intermediate; usually longer than those of *V. riviniana* but considerably shorter and broader than those of *V. lactea*, truncate, rounded or with a slightly cordate base.	Leaves ovate-lanceolate, truncate, rounded or cuneate at base
Corollas blue-violet often with dark zone on lip, immediately below the white throat.	Corollas variably intermediate in colour; often paler than in *V. riviniana* but more violet than in *V. lactea*; sometimes violet with paler patches; dark zone of *V. riviniana* sometimes present, sometimes not; same plant can have both types.	Corollas pale greyish-violet or almost white.
Spurs whitish, thick, scarcely tapering; notched.	Spurs yellowish; variably notched.	Spurs yellowish or greenish; notched or not.
Fertile, forming capsules.	Largely sterile, usually not forming capsules; dead, brown flowers remaining on plant.	Fertile, forming capsules.

Early Dog-violet

Viola reichenbachiana is most easily recognised by its dark, unnotched spur, its narrow upper petals which do not overlap, the little-branched veins of its lowest petal, its lanceolate, acute sepals and by the slight reddish tinge of the violet petals.

A perennial herb with a non-flowering but often fairly obvious leaf rosette (rosette leaves rather smaller than the stem leaves) which arises from a vertical rootstock and with aerial stems developing from around the rosette and reaching a height of 15 cm; often rather untidy in habit; stolons not present. **Petioles** glabrous or very slightly hairy. **Stipules** narrow; fimbriae long (distinctly longer than those of *V. riviniana*), especially higher up stem. **Leaves** ovate to broadly ovate, (1.5-)2.5-4.5(-5.0) cm long, up to 1.6 × as long as wide, crenate; mid to dark green in colour, sometimes slightly shiny; apex often acuminate; base cordate; blades with a small number of scattered white, patent hairs on upper surface but often not on the veins; increasing in size at fruiting time. **Pedicels** glabrous. **Bracteoles** at variable distances below bend of pedicel; narrow and lanceolate; often reddish in colour. **Sepals** green dotted with brown; lanceolate, pointed; appendages very short, < 1.5 mm long, not increasing in size as the fruit matures

V. reichenbachiana, *showing the narrow upper petals, the dark spur and the slight reddish cast to the corolla.* Photo: P. Stroh.

Viola reichenbachiana.

and becoming insignificant. **Flowers** unscented; usually pale violet, often with slight reddish tinge, very occasionally white (var. *leucantha*); corollas to 2.5 mm high with petals not overlapping; upper petals narrow, often twisted or folded back, sometimes giving the impression of 'rabbit's ears'; lateral petals narrow, bearded; lowest petal with a dark zone below white throat and unbranched or scarcely branching dark veins (sometimes one vein has one branch). **Spurs** straight, slender; dark purple, usually appreciably darker than corolla; unnotched. **Capsules** trigonous, pointed, less than 10 mm in length; glabrous; containing *c.* 12 seeds; dark brown in colour. **Flowering** late February or early March to end of April. **Chromosome number** 2n = 20.

Side view of the corolla of V. reichenbachiana *showing the dark unnotched spur, the lanceolate sepals and the folded back upper petals. Photo: J.R. Crellin.*

V. reichenbachiana is common in suitable habitat over much of England and Ireland, although absent from the far south-west of England and thinning out rapidly in the far north. It appears to be less common in western parts of Ireland. It is absent from many upland areas of Wales, although frequent to abundant when ecological conditions are appropriate. It is absent from Scotland as a native plant except in the south-west where it is rare. In mainland Europe it is

V. reichenbachiana *showing the stipules with long fimbriae.*

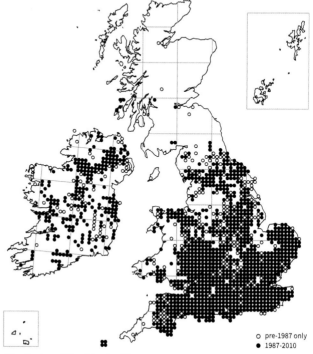

o pre-1987 only
● 1987-2010

Distribution of V. reichenbachiana.

widely distributed, occurring from Spain east to the Caucasus and from Greece in the south to as far north as southern Sweden. It is said to occur up to an altitude of 2,200 m in Switzerland.

V. reichenbachiana is a plant of deciduous woodlands (as indicated by both its French, Violette des bois, and German, Waldveilchen, vernacular names), hedge banks or woodland edges. It is rarely found in the open, although it can survive in such situations following woodland clearance. Its preference is for calcareous or base-rich soils and it is often frequent in woods over chalk or limestone or base-rich clays. In general it is a lowland plant, although it has been recorded as a native at an altitude of 245 m in Cumbria (Halliday, 1997) and as an introduction at 610 m in Perthshire. It has a much more limited range than its close relative *V. riviniana*.

V. reichenbachiana showing the corolla with little-branched veins and the folded back upper petals.

The conservation status in Britain is Least Concern (Cheffings & Farrell, 2005) and is the same in England (Stroh *et al.*, 2014) and, provisionally, in Ireland (M.B. Wyse Jackson pers. comm., 2015). Although there has been some decline in the northern parts of its range in Britain, there appear to be no specific threats.

V. reichenbachiana is present in the NVC **W8** *Fraxinus excelsior-Acer campestre-Mercurialis perennis* woodland community (Rodwell, 1991-2000).

Typical V. reichenbachiana *habitat at flowering time, showing the low vegetation and open woodland of early spring before the canopy closes over.*

Associates include *Alliaria petiolata, Arum maculatum, Corylus avellana, Fraxinus excelsior, Mercurialis perennis, Oxalis acetosella, Primula vulgaris, Ficaria verna* and *Viola riviniana*

First described by Jordan in 1857, the first British reference to the plant may be that of A.G. More in 1861 (More, 1861).

Notes

Flowering – V. reichenbachiana is the second *Viola* to come into flower in spring, somewhat later than *V. odorata* which is often in flower in early February, but usually about two weeks before its close relative *V. riviniana* and sometimes simultaneously with *V. hirta*. Its main flowering period is thus late February to April, although in some years it can still be found flowering in early May. When it normally comes into flower its woodland habitat is still open and relatively unshaded and associated plants are still small and undeveloped. Thus it can often be seen growing in almost bare earth or among mosses and dead leaves, its small leaf and flower clumps developing on the end of the partially exposed rhizome.

Insect food plant – V. reichenbachiana is thought to be a food plant for the larvae of the Dark Green Fritillary *Argynnis aglaja* and possibly other fritillaries.

Infraspecific taxa and hybrids

- hybridises with *V. riviniana* (*V.* × *bavarica*) (see **4 × 5**)
- hybridises with *V. canina* (though perhaps not in the British Isles) (see **5 × 6**)

Several colour variants have been recorded but only one, sometimes called var. *leucantha* Beck, is normally seen and this only rarely. The corolla is usually pure white with obscure veining on the lowest petal. The spur is white.

White variant of V. reichenbachiana *(var.* leucantha*). Photo: B.A. Tregale.*

Viola reichenbachiana × *V. canina*

Two characteristics of the parent species suggest that this hybrid will occur only rarely. Firstly, the very different habitats favoured by the two parents with *V. reichenbachiana* preferring wooded habitat on calcareous or base-rich soils whilst *V. canina* prefers open habitat on acid soils. Secondly, the difference in flowering times with *V. reichenbachiana* flowering from March to early May whilst *V. canina* usually flowers later, from May to June. As far as we can ascertain there have been no confirmed records since 1927, all later records being described as 'dubious'. The five records before 1927 were determined as such by E.S. Gregory but she appears subsequently to have had doubts about their validity and one of these specimens was later re-determined by Becker as *V. riviniana*. Nor does Gregory give a precise description of this hybrid in her monograph (Gregory, 1912). Additionally, Valentine (1975) saw no naturally-occurring specimens of this hybrid.

We feel, therefore, that there is no conclusive proof that this plant now occurs in Britain and Ireland, although the situation may possibly have been different when *V. canina* was more widespread, particularly in the south of England. We have, therefore, decided to provide no description for it.

Outside Britain and Ireland *Viola* × *mixta* has been recorded in central Europe and possibly elsewhere in mainland Europe but records are sparse and often uncertain. However, *Flora Nordica* reports it from Denmark and Sweden describing specimens from the latter country as 'plausible' (Jonsell & Karlsson, 2010). This Flora also notes that this taxon is 'closely similar to *V. canina* × *riviniana* (and therefore difficult to distinguish from it when the two are compared as herbarium specimens) but with more lilac flowers'.

Heath Dog-violet

Viola canina is characterised by its bluish or bluish-grey flowers, the absence of a dark zone on the lowest petal, its yellow spur, its dark green, shiny, more or less triangular leaves and the absence of a central non-flowering rosette.

A more or less glabrous perennial herb, with neither stolons nor a leaf rosette, all leaves being on the flowering stems. **Petioles** glabrous. **Stipules** long-triangular (up to 1/3 length of the petiole); with usually forward-pointing, sparse, short teeth, usually lacking fimbriae. **Leaves** more or less triangular in shape, becoming narrower and less triangular higher up stem but generally < 2 × as long as wide (often no more than 1.6 × as long as wide), less variable in length than the leaves of other *Viola* species (1.0-)1.4-3.0(-5.0) cm; dark green, with shallowly crenate edges; thick, often shiny; strongly reticulate beneath; apex blunt, occasionally sub-acute; base truncate or shallowly cordate, sometimes decurrent; glabrous or with very sparse short hairs. **Pedicels** glabrous. **Bracteoles** near top of pedicels; lanceolate. **Sepals** long and pointed; appendages large and spreading. **Flowers** unscented; often, but not always, blue or slate-blue, lacking the violet

V. canina *showing bluish flowers with yellow spurs and triangular leaves.*

Viola canina.

V. canina *seeding at Mawbray Dunes, Cumbria (May 2011), showing the dark green, shiny, triangular leaves with their reticulate under-surfaces. Note also the trigonous seed capsules with their large, patent sepal appendages (especially top right).*

tint found in other species of *Viola* but very occasionally deep violet (on dunes in Norfolk and maybe elsewhere); corollas to 22 mm but larger (and paler) in plants from some East Anglian fens (see subsp. *montana* below); upper and lateral petals obovate, roughly 1.5-2 × as long as broad; lowest petal lacking dark zone; veins little branched. **Spurs** thick, straight; yellow (often strikingly and conspicuously so), occasionally more greenish; usually deeply notched but occasionally not. **Capsules** trigonous, to 9 mm; glabrous; containing *c.* 20 seeds. **Flowering** April to May, occasionally June. **Chromosome number** 2n = 40.

V. canina is widely but very thinly distributed throughout Britain and Ireland, being very locally common only in parts of northern Scotland, the New Forest and on some coastal dunes. It is very rare or absent in many inland areas. In mainland Europe it is found from Spain to northern Scandinavia and east through France, Italy, Greece. Elsewhere it occurs from Turkey across to Siberia.

V. canina is a plant of unshaded often, but not exclusively, acidic habitats, occurring on coastal sand dunes, heathland, sandy inland

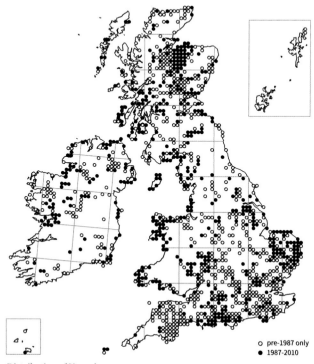

o pre-1987 only
● 1987-2010

Distribution of V. canina.

grassland and in close-cropped turf, on stony or shingly lake shores and in seasonally wet hollows nearby, in cracks in riverside rocks and on river shingles. It has also been reported as growing on soils overlying chalk where these have been leached by heavy rain and snow and at a number of its riverside sites it occurs on basic rocks. It occurs from sea-level or slightly above to altitudes of up to 600 m (in the Cairngorms).

The conservation status in Britain is Near Threatened (Cheffings & Farrell, 2005) whilst in England it is now considered Vulnerable (Stroh *et al.*, 2014). In Ireland it is provisionally classified as Least Concern (M.B. Wyse Jackson, pers. comm., 2015). Over the past 60 years *V. canina* has suffered a steep and continuing decline, especially at its inland sites. This decline has come about largely as a result of habitat loss and changes in agricultural practices, such as the drainage and improvement of rough grassland. Other causes may well be under- and over-grazing resulting perhaps from successive changes in the European Agricultural Policy. Further losses may be through hybridisation with the much more catholic and ubiquitous *V. riviniana* which very often grows in close association with *V. canina* but can tolerate a much greater range of soil types.

Corolla of V. canina *showing the blue (rather than violet) colour of the petals, the broad, obovate upper petals, the absence of dark zone below the little-branched veins on the lowest petal and, behind the corolla, the notched, yellow spur.*

NVC communities in which *V. canina* is present include **SD7** *Ammophila arenaria-Festuca rubra* semi-fixed dune community, **SD11** *Carex arenaria-Cornicularia aculeata* dune community and **CG11** *Festuca ovina-Agrostis capillaris-Alchemilla alpina* grass-heath (Rodwell, 1991-2000).

Commonly associated species include *Agrostis capillaris*, *Ammophila arenaria*, *Anthoxanthum odoratum*, *Arenaria serpyllifolia*, *Calluna vulgaris*, *Carex arenaria*, *C. flacca*, *Conopodium majus*, *Festuca rubra*, *F. ovina*, *Galium verum*, *Leontodon hispidus*, *Lotus corniculatus*, *Luzula multiflora*, *Molinia caerulea*, *Potentilla erecta* and *Viola riviniana*.

It was apparently first recorded (and illustrated) in 1724 near Mitcham, Surrey (v.c. 17 Surrey) by D. Du-Bois '*Violae caninae varietatem, si non speciem diversam*' (Ray, 1724).

Notes

Flower colour – Typically, the colour of the flowers of *V. canina* is blue or slate-blue rather than violet and this is often a key diagnostic character. However, there are exceptions with the corollas of plants often described as subsp. *montana* being consistently a paler blue than is usual, and some plants of subsp. *canina* growing on the coastal dunes of Norfolk being a much deeper violet (R. Leaney, pers. comm.).

Flowering – *V. canina* is one of the later blooming violets, its flowering season usually beginning in April and continuing until the end of May or early June. It is thus later than *V. riviniana* and earlier than its close relative *V. lactea*, although in both cases there is some overlap. It seems that plants growing on coastal sand dunes may come into flower earlier than those growing in inland sites.

Historical distribution – The decline of *V. canina* noted above is probably only the latest stage in a steady reduction in numbers, particularly at inland sites, that has been continuing since the early post glacial period. In a study on inland populations of *V. canina* in south-eastern Scotland and north-western England, Corner suggests that, with the abundance of open habitats and the unleached soil in the immediate post-glacial period, *V. canina,* which is intolerant of shade, was a widespread species. However, as forests expanded during the Boreal period numbers were sharply reduced. Relict populations were able to survive in the *refugia* provided by the small areas of relatively basic waterside habitat which probably never bore closed woodland (Corner, 1989). Some of these still survive today but they are fragile and extremely vulnerable.

Species circumscription – Although there are a number of clear differences between *V. canina* and *V. riviniana*, the two were originally classified together by Linnaeus, along with the species we know as *V. reichenbachiana* and *V. rupestris*, under the umbrella name of *V. canina*.

Infraspecific taxa and hybrids

- subsp. *montana* (L.) Hartm.
- subsp. *montana* hybridises with subsp. *canina*
- hybridises with *V. riviniana* (*V. × intersita*) (see **4 × 6**)
- hybridises with *V. reichenbachiana* (*V. × mixta*) (see **5 × 6**)
- hybridises with *V. lactea* (*V. × militaris*) (see **6 × 7**)
- hybridises with *V. stagnina* (*V. × ritschliana*) (see **6 × 8**)

The subspecies of *Viola canina*

Although usually growing in well-drained, open habitats, *V. canina* is also found in damper or even wet, occasionally shaded, sites. Plants growing in such sites, in the fens of East Anglia, have often been referred to the subspecies *montana*.

Upright growth habit of V. canina subsp. montana.

The plant described as *V. canina* subsp. *montana* is more erect with longer internodes, larger, paler corollas on longer pedicels, longer leaves (usually more than twice as long as wide) and longer stipules than *V. canina* subsp. *canina* (to half the length of the petiole, occasionally more). This is now found in wet, peaty ground at only two sites in Cambridgeshire: Holme Fen (v.c. 29 Cambs.) and Woodwalton Fen (v.c. 31 Hunts.), although it formerly occurred at Wicken Fen, also Cambridgeshire (v.c. 29 Cambs.), and in Suffolk, Lincolnshire and Nottinghamshire. However, there are differences between the plants found at these sites. The Holme Fen site which is damp and somewhat shaded has tall plants which fit well with the classic description above. Woodwalton Fen, which is wet but open and largely unshaded, has plants which are much closer to subsp. *canina* in leaves, internodes and stipules (perhaps showing evidence of hybridisation with subsp. *canina*). At both sites, however, the flowers are larger and paler than those of subsp. *canina*.

Although such plants do differ from subsp. *canina*, it has been suggested that these differences do not warrant subspecific status. It has been noted that in Britain and Ireland and, particularly, in mainland Europe there are plants which are intermediate between the two described subspecies and do not fit either description and that the two are completely interfertile (Jonsell & Karlsson, 2010).

V. canina subsp. montana *showing long internodes, long leaves and long stipules.*

Additionally, work by Bergdolt in a comparative growth experiment, showed that many features considered diagnostic of the subspecies of *V. canina* may be induced by habitat factors. For example, stipule size and shape could be manipulated by altering the availability of water and nutrients, and leaf-blade shape and texture by altering the light intensity (Bergdolt, 1932).

However, we consider that the morphological differences of the East Anglian plants from subsp. *canina* and their occupation of a distinctly different ecological niche (damper and more shaded than is usual with subsp. *canina*) justify the retention of subspecific status. This is supported by small scale experiments which show that plants removed from one of the East Anglian sites and grown on in conditions more suited to subsp. *canina* retain their morphological differences. However, we believe that further work on this subspecies is urgently needed, but at least, until morphometric studies have been completed, we feel the plant's subspecific status should be maintained.

It is interesting to note that in continental Europe the habitat of subsp. *montana* is much more varied and often very different from that in England. It is found in forests and on their edges, in dryish meadows and in mountain pastures in subalpine zones, as well as in fens. One online Flora says it occurs in the same habitat as subsp. *canina* (Info Flora Genève, 2004-2015). Complications arise as some continental workers give the name *V. canina* subsp. *ruppii* to (mainly) high altitude populations of the plant while others maintain that this name is synonymous with subsp. *montana*.

Flowers of V. canina *subsp. montana at Holme Fen. Photo: P. Stroh.*

Notes

Conservation status – *V. canina* subsp. *montana* is considered to be Endangered in England (Wigginton, 1999; Cheffings & Farrell, 2005; Stroh *et al.*, 2014). It is thus 'facing a very high risk of extinction in the wild'. It is not known to occur in Ireland, Scotland or Wales.

Nomenclature – It is now generally accepted that the name *Viola canina* subsp. *montana* (= *V. montana*) has for many years been misapplied (Van den Hof *et al.*, 2010) and should be replaced. However, as yet no new combination has been validly published.

Viola canina × V. lactea

Viola × *militaris* is a vigorous and sometimes tall-growing hybrid which is generally intermediate between its parents, although it often has internodes which are longer than those of either parent and some variants seen recently in West Cork seem much closer to *V. lactea*. The leaves, which appear closer to those of *V. lactea*, are considerably longer than broad (occasionally nearly twice as long) with bases which may be rounded, truncate or cuneate but are never cordate. The stipules are fimbriate, as in *V. lactea,* but have only a small number of teeth, being closer to *V. canina* in this respect. The flowers tend to be pale but have a bluish, rather than purplish tinge and the petals have a length/breadth ratio much closer to *V. canina* than to *V. lactea*. Unlike *V. riviniana* × *lactea*, this hybrid is partially fertile and capsules are sometimes formed (Moore, 1958), although T. O'Mahony (pers. comm.) reports that flowers of this taxon from Lough Allua, West Cork which he collected and dissected in the 1990s were all highly pollen-sterile.

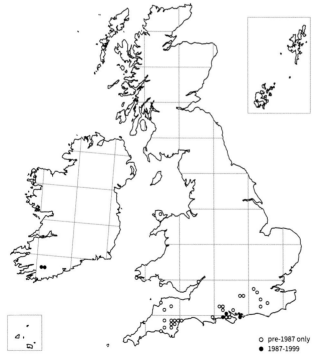

O pre-1987 only
● 1987-1999

Distribution of V. × militaris.

Corolla of Viola × militaris *showing the pale flowers and long leaves. Photo: T. O'Mahony.*

The only sites where *V.* × *militaris* has been reliably recorded in the past 50 years are where the two parents co-exist, in Hampshire, England (v.c. 11 S. Hants.) and Cork, Ireland (v.c. H3 W. Cork). It is thus today a very rare hybrid. In the nineteenth and twentieth centuries it was recorded widely, if sparsely, from western and southern England, North and South Wales and southern Ireland. Indeed, Francis Rose knew it in a number of sites especially in Hampshire. In mainland Europe it has been recorded in France and Spain.

The habitat of *V.* × *militaris* is best described as dry-heath but, in Ireland, at Lough Allua, West Cork, it occurs in the transition zone between the lake margin habitat where *V. canina* grows and the dry-heath which supports *V. lactea* (T. O'Mahony, pers. comm.). Moore (1958) states that, although the pH requirements of the parents do not differ greatly, *V. lactea* requires a much less base-rich soil with a higher humus content than *V. canina*. He suggests that the ecological barriers created by this are rarely breached, perhaps only in areas that have suffered some disturbance, with the parents rarely growing together. It therefore seems likely that at least some of the records for this hybrid are misidentifications of the much more common (and variable) hybrid between *V. riviniana* and *V. lactea*.

Notes

Identification – There is no single character which distinguishes this hybrid from its parents or from *V. riviniana* × *lactea*, so, even more than with other *Viola* hybrids, a suite of characters should be used.

Triple hybrid? – One of T. O'Mahony's specimens from Lough Allua has soboles (never found in either *V. canina* or *V. lactea*) which suggests that it may be a triple hybrid with *V. riviniana* also involved, although this possibility would need to be confirmed by molecular work. Whether such a situation obtains elsewhere is a matter for further study.

Viola canina	*Viola* × *militaris*	*Viola lactea*
Stipules small, less than half as long as petiole, serrate-dentate, not fimbriate.	Stipules small, less than half as long as the petiole, few teeth but some distinctly fimbriate.	Upper stipules large, equalling or occasionally exceeding petiole, fimbriate-serrate.
Leaves 1.0-1.6 × as long as wide.	Leaves up to 1.9 × as long as wide but often much less.	Leaves 2.0-3.0 × as long as wide.
Leaf bases truncate or shallowly cordate.	Leaf bases rounded, truncate or cuneate (never cordate).	Leaf bases rounded or cuneate.
Corollas blue.	Corollas creamy with blue (rather than violet) tinge.	Corollas creamy to pale lilac.
Petals 1.5-2.0 × as long as broad.	Petals 1.5-2.0 × as long as broad.	Petals *c*. 3 × as long as broad.
Capsules with fertile seeds produced.	Occasionally produces small, often deformed, capsules with a small number of fertile seeds.	Capsules with fertile seeds produced.

Viola canina × *V. stagnina*

It seems likely that both subspecies of *V. canina* hybridise with *V. stagnina* in our area. The hybrid involving subsp. *canina* is rare but occurs in both England and Ireland. The hybrid involving subsp. *montana* is extremely rare and is thought to have occurred at only two sites, at Wicken Fen and Woodwalton Fen in Cambridgeshire; there are no recent records.

Viola canina subsp. *canina* × *V. stagnina*

Viola × *ritschliana* is, in flower shape and colour, closer to *V. canina* subsp. *canina* but has leaves which are more elongated and with larger stipules. In comparison to *V. stagnina* the flowers are deeper blue with slightly longer whitish spurs which may also be decurved (C.L. O'Reilly pers. obs. in Stace *et al.* (2015)). This hybrid also possesses soboles similar to *V. stagnina* and may form vigorous plants which can

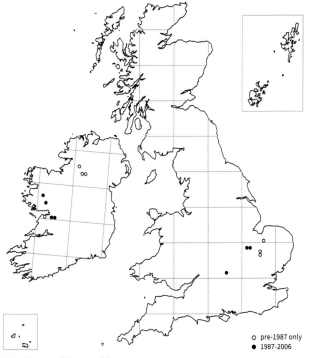

○ pre-1987 only
● 1987-2006

Distribution of V. × ritschliana.

V. × ritschliana *at Otmoor, Oxfordshire. The flower colour and leaf shape and size of the hybrid exhibit intermediacy between the parents.*

reproduce vegetatively but are always sterile with brown shrivelled flowers remaining on the plant sometimes long after flowering, and with capsules failing to form.

V. × ritschliana can occur where *V. stagnina* and *V. canina* subsp. *canina* grow in reasonably close proximity, but, because of the rarity of *V. stagnina*, it has been recorded at very few sites in England. At Otmoor, Oxfordshire (v.c. 23 Oxon) and, in Cambridgeshire, Woodwalton Fen (v.c. 31 Hunts.) and Wicken Fen (v.c. 29 Cambs.) the hybrid appears to occupy (or have occupied) a slightly drier habitat than *V. stagnina*. In Ireland, where it is a little less rare, it has been recorded on the shores of Upper Lough Erne, Fermanagh (v.c. H33 Fermanagh) and in the rather specialised habitat at the margins of turloughs (lakes with fluctuating water levels) in both Fermanagh and the Burren, County Clare (v.c. H9 Co. Clare). Here, *V. canina* subsp. *canina* is found in a higher drier zonal layer than *V. stagnina* which occupies a lower layer close to the water. The hybrid, which is relatively frequent, occurs in the intermediate zone between the two. *V. × ritschliana* is widespread in central and northern Europe as far north as southern Sweden.

Viola stagnina	Viola × ritschliana	Viola canina subsp. canina
Soboles present.	Soboles often present.	Soboles never present.
Stipules to 20 mm long, not exceeding the petiole.	Stipules similar to *V. stagnina*.	Stipules small, less than half as long as petiole, serrate-dentate, not fimbriate.
Leaves 2-4 × as long as wide.	Leaves 2-3 × as long as wide.	Leaves 1-1.6 × as long as wide.
Leaves ovate to lanceolate, pale green.	Leaves ovate to lanceolate, medium green.	Leaves ± triangular, dark green.
Corollas pale blue to almost white.	Corollas light blue, intermediate between parents but closer to *V. canina*.	Corollas blue.
Spurs pale green, straight.	Spurs whitish-green, sometimes decurved.	Spurs yellow to greenish-yellow, straight.

A turlough at Mullaghmore in the Burren, where V. stagnina, V. canina *subsp.* canina *and their hybrid* V. × ritschliana *occur in different zonal layers at the margin.*

Viola canina **subsp.** *montana* × *V. stagnina*

Definite records for this taxon are extremely rare and come mainly from the first half of the twentieth century. At Wicken Fen, Cambridgeshire (v.c. 29 Cambs.) the hybrid between *V. ericetorum* (now *V. canina*) and *V. stagnina* was recorded in 1900 by A. Wallis and the herbarium specimen (**CGE**) subsequently re-determined as 'probably *V. canina* subsp. *montana* × *persicifolia*' by the late S.M. Walters. As subsp. *canina* has apparently never been recorded at Wicken Fen this hybrid is highly likely to involve subsp. *montana*. Also in Cambridgeshire subsp. *montana* occurs at Holme Fen (v.c. 31 Hunts.), from where *V. stagnina* has long since disappeared, and Woodwalton Fen (v.c. 31 Hunts.) where subsp. *canina* also occurs. At Holme Fen there is no evidence of the past or present existence of the subsp. *montana* × *V. stagnina* hybrid. At Woodwalton Fen, however, Gregory (1912) says that intermediates between *V. canina* subsp. *canina*, *V. canina* subsp. *montana* and *V. stagnina* were frequent. More recently, S.M. Walters, from his own observations at Woodwalton Fen during the period 1945-1965, notes the 'bewildering array of 'fen violets' referable to *V. persicifolia* (now *V. stagnina*), *V. canina* subsp. *montana*, and the sterile hybrid' Walters (1999). At Otmoor in Oxfordshire (v.c. 23 Oxon) there is some uncertainty as to whether *V. canina* subsp. *montana* actually occurs there and as a consequence this particular hybrid is considered absent from that site.

With such a limited amount of material to work on and with the many similarities between the two subspecies, we feel unable to give full details to distinguish between the hybrid with subsp. *montana* from that with subsp. *canina*. Presumably the former may be a taller plant with longer internodes, pedicels, leaves and stipules, but, as hybrids are variable and the *V. stagnina* parent itself differs from subsp. *canina* in some of the characters exhibited by subsp. *montana*, determination will always be problematic. An examination of Wallis' specimen at CGE offers little further clarification. Perhaps the uncertainty shown by Walters in naming this specimen, despite his many years of intimate knowledge of all these plants, suggests that in many cases it may be impossible to distinguish them.

Pale Dog-violet

Viola lactea is characterised by the pale violet, often almost white flowers growing on long stalks, the long dark green lanceolate or ovate-lanceolate leaves with truncate or rounded bases and the stout, yellowish spur.

A subglabrous perennial herb with no central rosette, rhizomes or stolons; aerial stems few, to 30 cm high, although often much less. **Petioles** glabrous. **Stipules** long, lanceolate; usually with short, stout teeth sometimes somewhat fimbriate towards base; sometimes equalling or exceeding length of petioles of upper leaves but much shorter than longer petioles of middle and lower leaves. **Leaves** lanceolate or ovate-lanceolate, (1.0-)1.5-3.5(-4.0) cm long, usually from *c.* 2-3 × as long as broad; thick, bluntly toothed; dark green; apex subacute; base cuneate, truncate, or rounded (but see hybrid with *V. riviniana*); leaves and petioles sometimes tinged with purple. **Pedicels** glabrous, long. **Bracteoles** just below bend of pedicel; insignificant; sometimes slightly toothed. **Sepals** lanceolate; appendages large, almost half as long as spurs. **Flowers** unscented; pale, milky violet, often almost white with a violet tinge; corollas to 20 mm; upper and lateral petals narrow, 2-3 × as long as wide; lowest petal with deep purple, well branched veins and apiculate tip. **Spurs** stout; yellowish; notched or not. **Capsules** round-trigonous, to 8 mm in length; glabrous. **Flowering** May to June. **Chromosome number** 2n = 60.

V. lactea *showing the very pale flowers, the lanceolate, dark green leaves and the yellowish, notched spur.* Photo: J. R. Crellin.

Viola lactea.

The corolla of V. lactea *showing the almost white petals with the slightest hint of violet, the branched purple veins on the lowest petal and the long pedicel.*

V. lactea is found essentially in the south and west of Britain and Ireland. It reaches its northern limit near the coast on Anglesey, occurs along the west and south coasts of Wales, in the West Country and along the south coast of England, with concentrations in Pembrokeshire, Cornwall, Dorset and the New Forest. It occurs, almost exclusively along the coast, in the southern part of the Ireland with a concentration in Co. Kerry. Populations situated outside these areas have died out and even in the south and west of England there appears to have been a withdrawal towards the coast. In mainland Europe *V. lactea* also has an oceanic distribution, occurring along the Atlantic coast of France, Spain and Portugal and reaching as far south as the River Tagus in Portugal.

V. lactea is a lowland plant, all populations being below an altitude of 240 m, usually occurring on shallow, dry, well-drained, acid soils in sites exposed to wind and sun. However, it is sometimes found in much wetter sites which may be partially waterlogged in winter, for instance Penrhosfeilw Common on Anglesey and several sites in South Wales. Many of its sites are close to the coast and maritime conditions may be beneficial to its growth, as well as offering some protection from hard frosts and severe winters of which it is intolerant. Its preferred

Leaves of V. lactea, *showing the ovate-lanceolate shape and the cuneate base. The slight purplish flushing on the underside of the leaf can also be detected.*

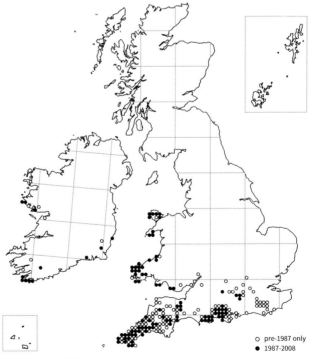

○ pre-1987 only
● 1987-2008

Distribution of V. lactea.

conditions occur on nutrient-poor inland or maritime heathland, patchy grassland and along track sides where the soil pH is in the range of 4.7 to 6.5 (Moore, 1958).

The conservation status in Britain is Vulnerable (Cheffings & Farrell, 2005) but it is considered Endangered in England (Stroh *et al.*, 2014). In Ireland it is provisionally classified as 'Near Threatened at least, Vulnerable likely' (M.B. Wyse Jackson, pers. comm., 2015). It is not known to occur in Northern Ireland (Preston *et al.*, 2002). *V. lactea* suffered many losses during the twentieth century, although these were slightly offset by the discovery of new sites in Wales. It is thought that this decline has resulted from habitat loss and inappropriate land management, particularly the application of fertilisers, and a failure to deal with the encroachment of scrub in the plant's favoured habitats. It is a poor competitor and, having little tolerance of shade, dies out where sites are not kept open by cattle-grazing, controlled burning or clearing. It can thus benefit greatly from careful site management such as gorse removal. It frequently does well in sites which have been subject to some disturbance and appears to thrive after burning. A further problem has arisen because of hybridisation with the far more ubiquitous *V. riviniana* which is able to thrive in similar habitats to *V. lactea*. In a number of *V. lactea* sites the frequency of the hybrid between these two species is steadily increasing, to the detriment of both parental species which are out-competed by their vigorous offspring. *V. riviniana*, with its much more catholic habitat-preference, is globally little affected whereas *V. lactea* which has a very limited ecological niche suffers much more severely.

NVC communities in which *V. lactea* occurs include **H3** *Ulex minor-Agrostis curtisii* heath, **H4** *Ulex gallii-Agrostis curtisii* heath, **H6** *Erica vagans-Ulex europaeus* heath and **H8** *Calluna vulgaris-Ulex gallii* heath (Rodwell, 1991-2000).

The lanceolate stipule of V. lactea *with sparse teeth, which tend to become somewhat fimbriate below.*

An unopened V. lactea *flower showing large sepal appendages and yellowish spur.*

Typical V. lactea *heathland habitat on Anglesey.*

Frequent associates of *V. lactea* typically include *Calluna vulgaris*, *Erica cinerea*, *Festuca ovina*, *Pedicularis sylvatica* (in wetter sites), *Pilosella officinarum*, *Plantago lanceolata*, *Polygala serpyllifolia*, *Potentilla erecta*, *Scilla verna* (on maritime heaths), *Thymus polytrichus*, *Ulex gallii* and *Viola riviniana*.

V. lactea seems to have been first found by Mr Stackhouse at Pendarvis, Cornwall (v.c. 1a W. Cornwall), in about 1796 (Withering, 1796) and was also described by J.E. Smith in 1798 in his *English Botany* (Smith, 1798). His description is based on a specimen found near Tunbridge Wells in Kent (v.c. 16 W. Kent) by T.F. Forster.

Note

Flowering – Flowering begins in May and sometimes continues until late June. This flowering period begins significantly later than that of the closely allied *V. canina* (April to May) and is even later than *V. riviniana* (late March to May) but there is some overlap leading to hybridisation with both these species.

Infraspecific taxa and hybrids

- hybridises with *V. riviniana* (see **4 × 7**)
- hybridises with *V. canina* (*V. × militaris*) (see **6 × 7**)

86

Viola lactea at Cors Goch, Anglesey. Photo: J.R. Crellin.

Fen Violet

Viola stagnina is characterised in having aerial stems arising from creeping rhizomes, leaf blades ovate-lanceolate, very much longer than wide, flowers with +/- flat corollas, very pale blue to almost white petals, and a greenish spur.

A subglabrous perennial herb lacking a central flowering rosette but with underground creeping soboles. **Petioles** glabrous or slightly hairy; erect, to 25 cm. **Stipules** lanceolate, to 20 mm long; hairy; coarsely toothed; not exceeding petiole. **Leaves** narrowly ovate to lanceolate, blade 2-4 cm long, 2-4 × as long as wide, pale green; margins crenate with forward-pointing teeth; apex acute; base truncate to subcordate; slightly hairy on upper surface, glabrous beneath. **Pedicels** glabrous; to 3 cm. **Bracteoles** towards top of pedicel. **Sepals** lanceolate, acute; appendages relatively large, suborbicular. **Flowers** singly from upper part of aerial stem; corollas 10-15 mm, appearing almost flat, slightly higher than wide; petals very pale blue to almost white with light violet veins; upper petals recurved, obovate, to 13 mm, lateral petals similar with hyaline hairs in the throat. **Spurs** saccate, 2-4 mm long, about as long as wide; pale green; 2-3.5 × as long as sepal appendages. **Capsules** ovoid, 6-8 mm long; glabrous. **Flowering** late April to mid-May. **Chromosome number** 2n = 20.

In England, *V. stagnina* was known from more than twenty sites in fens and river valleys, mostly in eastern England, but nowadays it appears to have been lost from Norfolk, Suffolk, Yorkshire, Lincolnshire and Nottinghamshire. By the early 1990s its only remaining sites were

V. stagnina *at Otmoor, showing corolla with pale blue, obovate petals and ovate-lanceolate leaves.*

Viola stagnina.

thought to be in Cambridgeshire at Woodwalton Fen (v.c. 31 Hunts.) and Wicken Fen (v.c. 29 Cambs.). However, by the beginning of the twenty-first century the plant was also in decline even at these sites with none found at Wicken Fen until 2014 when, after 15 barren years, up to 30 plants were seen, and only one plant at Woodwalton Fen in 2005 (although it is hoped that a viable seed bank at both sites will lead to regeneration under suitable management). Currently the strongest population is at Otmoor, Oxfordshire (v.c. 23 Oxon) where, in 1997, after an apparent absence of three decades, it was rediscovered in a fen meadow in ground which had been disturbed by the removal of willow scrub two years previously. In Ireland *V. stagnina* is recorded from the shores of Lough Erne and from turloughs in Fermanagh (v.c. H33 Fermanagh) and in the west is found in the Burren, Co. Clare (v.c. H9 Co. Clare) area on the sloping margins of turloughs (and at other lakes with fluctuating water levels). At the Burren turloughs it grows in association with *V. canina*, and the hybrid between them. Each occurs in separate zonal layers above the water level. On the European mainland, *V. stagnina* can be found in grazed vegetation and in the Czech Republic it is recorded on alluvial flood-plain meadows subject

V. stagnina *at Otmoor, showing the rather short, greenish spur.*

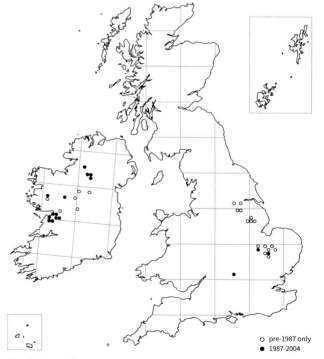

Distribution of V. stagnina.

○ pre-1987 only
● 1987-2004

Pressed specimens of V. stagnina. *The long coarsely-toothed stipules can clearly be seen.*

to annual inundation. In Scandinavia it occurs on gravelly lake shores, wet rock fissures, dried-out pools in forests, and in wet meadows. It is threatened there by the lack of grazing or mowing and by eutrophication and drainage. Worldwide, *V. stagnina* is mainly confined to the cool temperate regions of Europe and western Russia although it is also present from central Siberia southwards to the Altai Mountains. In Europe it is widely distributed from western Ireland to Russia and from Scandinavia to northern Spain.

At the current English sites the plants prefers wet, base-rich soils in fens and unimproved fen meadow. These soils overlay peat at the two Cambridgeshire sites and clay in Oxfordshire. Seasonally wet, rather than waterlogged, areas in relatively open vegetation are preferred, often with patches of bare soil. It does best where the surface is periodically disturbed and does not persist when the vegetation becomes dense. When peat was dug commercially in Cambridgeshire the plant would sometimes re-appear in large numbers near the excavations and it was abundant in the period around 1960-70 at Woodwalton Fen following clay excavation and the removal of carr. Measurements of pH at Wicken Fen ranged from 6.50 to 6.95 indicating a neutral to slightly acidic requirement for the plant.

The conservation status of *V. stagnina* in Britain is Endangered (Cheffings & Farrell, 2005) and is Critically Endangered in England (Stroh *et al.*, 2014). In Ireland it is, provisionally, classed as Near Threatened (M.B. Wyse Jackson, pers. comm., 2015). It is listed in Schedule 8 of the Wildlife and Countryside Act 1981. The current perilous state of *V. stagnina* in Britain is primarily due to the loss of its fen habitat with drainage and agricultural reclamation. At localities where it had been protected in the past, it is possible that the management had been inadequate in maintaining populations of viable self-sustaining size when the surrounding vegetation encroached and crowded it out. Another contribution to its demise might be its readiness to hybridise with *V. canina* to the detriment of maintaining a pure population. As a precaution, and to ensure future survival, seed from Otmoor and Wicken Fen has been preserved in the Millennium Seed Bank at Wakehurst Place (Kew). Living plants initially preserved at Oxford Botanic Gardens are thought not to have survived. It has declined throughout much of western Europe and is now rare in many countries. Although information is not available for all other European countries it is classified as Rare in Latvia and the Czech Republic, Vulnerable in Poland and Denmark, and Endangered in Netherlands, Lithuania and Switzerland. It is not considered to be threatened in Scandinavia.

At Wicken Fen, the habitat had an NVC classification of **M24** *Molinia-caerulea-Cirsium dissectum* fen-meadow. At Woodwalton, the classification was slightly different comprising an **MG10** *Holcus lanatus-Juncus effusus* rush-pasture and **M22** *Juncus subnodulosus-Cirsium palustre* fen-meadow. At Otmoor, the habitat which supports *V. stagnina* is quite varied, with abundant sedges and is perhaps closest to **M24** *Molinia-caerulea-Cirsium dissectum* fen-meadow, although not entirely typical of it (Rodwell, 1991-2000).

Different associated species are present at the three sites. At Wicken Fen *Calystgia sepium, Carex panicea, Cirsium palustre, Cladium mariscus, Epilobium hirsutum, Juncus subnodulosus, Mentha aquatica, Phalaris arundinacea* and *Phragmites australis*; at Woodwalton Fen *Agrostis stolonifera, Carex acutiformis, C. panicea, C. viridula, Hydrocotyle vulgaris, Juncus articulatus, J. effusus, J. subnodulosus* and *Ranunculus flammula*; at Otmoor *Agrostis canina, Carex panicea, Cirsium dissectum, Molinia caerulea* and *Viola canina*.

Corolla of V. stagnina *(Otmoor).*

Clarke (1900), under the name *V. persicifolia*, gives the first record for this plant from Lincolnshire (v.c. 53 S. Lincs.) in 1839 as 'found by Mr John Nicholson near Lincoln, and described as a state of *V. lactea*'. However, it had already been collected at Otmoor in Oxfordshire (v.c.

23 Oxon) in 1821, as there is a specimen from there by an unknown collector dated May 28th of that year which is preserved in the Oxford herbarium (**OXF**) (Druce, 1927). Another early record was at Whittlesey Mere in Cambridgeshire (v.c. 31 Hunts.) in 1824.

Notes

Nomenclature – For a long time, the name *V. persicifolia* has been used for this species but *V. persicifolia* Schreb. had also been applied to the European taxa *V. elatior* and *V. pumila*. To avoid any ambiguity, rejection of the name *V. persicifolia* was proposed by Danihelka *et al.* (2010) and the later name *V. stagnina* Kit. ex Schult. should now be used. Schultes (1814) described the plant in his Austrian Flora.

Historical distribution – *V. stagnina* is now extinct at most of the old sites where it was formerly recorded. In Cambridgeshire (v.c. 29 Cambs.) it was known at Bottisham, Ely, Sutton Dole, and Wimblington Fens, and also at Clayhythe, but it was lost from all these sites by the late nineteenth century, surviving only at Wicken Fen. Also in Cambridgeshire (v.c. 31 Hunts.), other than at Woodwalton Fen, it occurred at Holme Fen and Whittlesey Fen but again became extinct at both by the end of the nineteenth century. West Dereham Fen in Norfolk (v.c. 28 W. Norfolk)) was a locality where it was known until 1936 and it was present at Lakenheath, Suffolk (v.c. 26 W. Suffolk) until at least 1968. In Lincolnshire (v.c. 53 S. Lincs.) it was lost from Branston Fen and Potterhamworth as early as the nineteenth century but survived at Boultham until 1933 whilst, further north in the same county (v.c. 54 N. Lincs.), it could be found at Fiskerton and Woodhall Spa until about 1930. In Nottinghamshire (v.c. 56 Notts.) it occurred at Misson-Misterton only up to 1840 but survived at Bawtry and Newington-Misson much longer until as late as about 1950. South Yorkshire (v.c. 63 S. W. Yorks.) had two sites, one at Askern and the other near Thorne Woods, both of which survived until the middle of the twentieth century. In Oxfordshire (v.c. 23 Oxon), apart from the extant site Otmoor where it has been known since at least 1821, it also occurred at Menmarsh until 1964.

Infraspecific taxa and hybrids

- hybridises with *V. canina* subsp. *canina* (*V.* × *ritschliana*) (see **6 × 8**)

Marsh Violet

Viola palustris is characterised by its creeping underground stems from which the flowers and leaves arise on individual stalks, the, typically, lilac coloured flowers with a conspicuously veined lowest petal, the large reniform leaves and in its requirement for damp or wet habitats.

A perennial herb with long creeping rhizomes (unique in British and Irish violets) bearing rosettes of 3-4 leaves at the nodes; aerial stems absent. **Petioles** glabrous or variably hairy; long, sometimes up to 30 cm in length at end of summer. **Stipules** pale; broadly ovate to triangular; fringed with short glandular hairs. **Leaves** reniform to orbicular, (1.5-)2.0-4.0(-5.0) cm across at flowering, up to 7 cm or even more later in the summer; faintly toothed; apex obtuse, rarely subacute to ± acuminate; base cordate; glabrous. **Pedicels** glabrous, sometimes hairy towards base. **Bracteoles** situated at about middle of pedicel or slightly below; narrow, linear; insignificant. **Sepals** ovate, obtuse; appendages to 1 mm, obtuse. **Flowers** unscented (see note below); pale lilac, sometimes with pinkish tinge, occasionally all white; corolla to 15 mm; petals obovate; lowest petal with dark purple, much branched veins. **Spurs** obtuse; short but longer than appendages; concolorous with corolla; unnotched. **Capsules** ± trigonous, to 10 mm; glabrous. **Flowering** April to June, occasionally later. **Chromosome number** 2n = 48.

V. palustris showing creeping habit and typical leaf shape. Photo: F.J. Roberts.

V. palustris is widespread throughout much of Britain and Ireland but largely with a northern and western bias and absent from parts

Viola palustris.

The broad stipule of V. palustris.

Leaves of V. palustris *in July measuring slightly over 7 cm in length.*

of eastern and central England and from the Channel Islands where suitable habitats are lacking. It is also scarce in central Ireland. It has been recorded from sea-level to an altitude in excess of 1200 m on Ben Macdui in Scotland. In mainland Europe it occurs from northern Scandinavia to the Mediterranean region and from Portugal to the Balkans. It is also present in north Africa and on the North American continent.

V. palustris is a plant of acidic bogs, marshes, damp heaths, wet pastures, flushes, hillside runnels, stream sides and ditches. It is also found in *Alnus* and *Salix* carr and in wet woods where there is some flushing and where it thrives in partial shade. At all these sites it is often associated with *Sphagnum* mosses. Plants are also found in non-calcareous dune-slacks.

The conservation status in Britain is Least Concern (Cheffings & Farrell, 2005) and is the same in England (Stroh *et al.*, 2014) and, provisionally, in Ireland (M.B. Wyse Jackson, pers. comm., 2015). Losses have occurred, particularly in south-east England and central Ireland as a result of agricultural improvements, specifically the drainage of marshes and wet fields and the ploughing and reseeding of meadows.

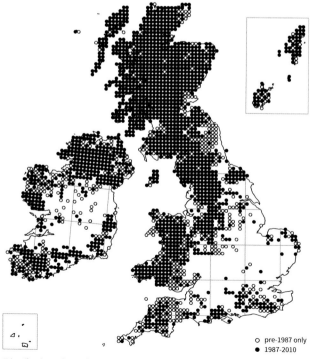

O pre-1987 only
● 1987-2010

Distribution of V. palustris.

In more boggy areas plants have been lost to peat extraction. These threats remain, particularly in lowland areas.

It occurs in many NVC mire communities, especially **M7** *Carex curta-Sphagnum russowii* mire and **M6** *Carex echinata* sub-community and *Juncus acutiflorus* sub-community but also in communities **M4-5**, **M8-9**, **M12**, **M15**, **M23-25**, **M27**, **M29**, **M31-32** and **M38**; woodland communities **W3** *Salix pentandra-Carex rostrata* woodland, **W4** *Betula pubescens-Molinia caerulea* woodland, **W5** *Alnus glutinosa-Carex paniculata* woodland and **W7** *Alnus glutinosa-Fraxinus excelsior-Lysimachia nemorum* woodland; swamp communities **S1** *Carex elata* sedge-swamp**,** **S3** *Carex paniculata* sedge-swamp and **S21** *Scirpus maritimus* swamp; grassland communities **CG11b** damp *Festuca ovina-Agrostis capillaris-Alchemilla alpina* grass-heath, **CG12** *Festuca ovina-Alchemilla alpina-Silene acaulis* dwarf-herb community; and upland communities especially **U14** *Alchemilla alpina-Sibbaldia procumbens* dwarf-herb community and **U18** *Cryptogramma crispa-Athyrium distentifolium* snow-bed but also **U4**, **U7**, **U10-11** and **U13** communities (Rodwell, 1991-2000).

V. palustris *growing out of moss, showing the heavy purple veining on the lowest petal and the large leaves. Photo: T. Melling.*

The wide range of associated species includes *Achillea ptarmica, Agrostis capillaris, Angelica sylvestris, Caltha palustris, Carex canescens, C. echinata, C. nigra, C. panicea, Epilobium palustre, Festuca ovina, Galium palustre, Juncus effusus, Lotus pedunculatus, Luzula multiflora, Stellaria uliginosa, Succisa pratensis* and *Veronica scutellata*.

The first reference appears to be that of the Reverend Stonehouse at Darfield in Yorkshire (v.c. 63 S. W. Yorks.) (Parkinson, 1640) where it was described as '*Viola rubra striata Eboracensis*'.

Notes

Flower scent – The flowers of *V. palustris* are normally assumed to be unscented but *Flora Nordica* describes them as having a 'honey-like scent'.

Insect food plant – *V. palustris* is one of the main larval food-plants of the Dark Green Fritillary *Argynnis aglaja*, the Silver-washed Fritillary *A. paphia*, the Pearl-bordered and the Small Pearl-bordered Fritillaries *Boloria euphrosyne* and *B. selene*.

Habitat – V. palustris, *though often found in open situations, also thrives in mossy woodland with dappled shade.*

Infraspecific taxa and hybrids

No hybrids involving *V. palustris* have been recorded in Britain or Ireland.

The subsp. *juressi* (Link ex Wein) Cout. is a very poorly differentiated taxon which may deserve varietal rank only. It has a confused and confusing history relating to how and whether it can be differentiated from subsp. *palustris* (and from *V. epipsila* Ledeb. in some countries) and exactly where it occurs in Europe.

Typical *V. palustris* subsp. *palustris* leaves are obtuse and glabrous, the petioles also glabrous, the bracteoles usually positioned below the middle of the pedicel, the spurs only slightly longer than the sepal appendages and the seed capsules with rounded tips. However, variants can be found which differ to varying degrees from the species. One variant has been named subsp. *juressi*. It is described as having summer leaves which are subacute to +/- acuminate, usually with patent hairs on the petioles, although these can sometimes be glabrous, bracteoles usually positioned above or towards the middle of the pedicel, the corolla and spur larger than in subsp. *palustris* and the capsules with pointed tips. The chromosome number of subsp. *juressi* is the same as that of subsp. *palustris* (2n = 48).

Flora Europaea gives the distribution of the taxon, subsp. *palustris*, as most of Europe, except for Portugal and the Azores, but rare in the south and east, while subsp. *juressi* is said to occur in 'Western Europe northwards to Ireland' (Tutin *et al.*, 1968). Both subspecies are found in Britain and Ireland but subsp. *juressi* has a pronounced westerly distribution, being more or less restricted to south-west England, south and west Wales and south and west Ireland. However, in a recent flora, Muñoz Garmendia (1993) firmly states that subsp. *juressi* does not merit subspecific status and that the only subspecies to be found in the Iberian Peninsula is subsp. *palustris*. Additionally, in France most botanists regard subsp. *juressi* as synonymous with *V. palustris* (Tison & de Foucault, 2014) or give it, at the most, varietal status (M. Espeut, pers. comm.).

The petioles of a specimen of V. palustris *from a site at 280 m in Wales showing the patent hairs, said to be one of the characters of subsp.* juressi.

In Britain and Ireland the situation may be different in that plants fitting closely with the above description of subsp. *juressi* can certainly be found. However, there are also numerous intermediate and contradictory variants which, for example, while possessing hairs on the petiole do not have the subacute leaves or a corolla larger than that of typical *V. palustris*. Similarly, there are other plants with large corollas which lack the hairy petioles of subsp. *juressi*. Additionally, the presence of hairs on the petiole (which is probably the clearest character on which to attempt a determination of this taxon) appears to be variable. Sites which have held plants with hairy petioles one year may possess glabrous ones the next, and plants with hairy petioles when moved from a mild to a colder climate can become glabrous after only one year. There is a significant comment in *Flora Nordica* regarding the presence of hairs which 'may vary much even within a single individual' (Jonsell & Karllson, 2010), a situation noted in plants growing at a high level in Wales (pers. obs.). Additionally, Chater states that subsp. *juressi* 'seems poorly differentiated and that intermediate plants showing one or two of the characters of subsp. *palustris* are often seen' (Chater, 2010). There have been suggestions that subsp. *juressi* is a plant of sheltered lowland sites but recent records of plants with hairy petioles from exposed hillsides at 280 m in North Wales (M.P. Wilcox, pers. comm.) show that this may not be the case.

The inconsistency in morphological characters combined with the lack of a specific ecological niche make it difficult to uphold subspecific status and, until further work has been carried out to resolve these anomalies, it seems better to regard *V. palustris* as a variable species with a broad range of characters and ecological preferences.

Horned Pansy

Viola cornuta is characterised by its long-stalked flowers, its well separated, rather narrow upper petals, its fragrance and, especially, by the very long (to 15 mm), slightly curved spur.

An introduced herbaceous perennial herb with a slender rhizome. **Petioles** ascending to 30(-80) cm. **Stipules** 0.5-1.5 cm, equalling or exceeding petiole; subtriangular; serrate to palmately-incised. **Leaves** ovate, 2-3 cm, crenate; apex acute; sparsely hairy on veins beneath and with a few scattered hairs on upper surface. **Pedicels** glabrous, to 30 cm. **Bracteoles** in top half of the pedicel, usually just below bend; small. **Sepals** acuminate, 12-18 mm × 1.0-2.5 mm; glabrous; appendages notched, large (> 3 mm long). **Flowers** fragrant; violet to lilac (wild and cultivated flowers) and white (cultivars only); corollas 2-4 cm wide; lateral petals subhorizontal, well separated; lower petal 21-34 mm, often white at the base. **Spurs** cylindrical, 10-15 mm,

The violet form of V. cornuta *growing in a garden, showing separated petals.*

Viola cornuta.

slightly curved; greatly exceeding (*c.* 6 ×) calyx appendages. **Capsules** 7-10 × 5 mm. **Flowering** April to June or later. **Chromosome number** 2n = 22.

V. cornuta is a garden plant grown for ornament which sometimes becomes naturalised in the wild on roadsides, wood-borders, grassy river-banks and railway embankments, and in hedgerows and rough grassland. It may also occur as a casual on waste ground and rubbish tips. It is generally a lowland plant, most of its sites being below 250 m. It is native to the Pyrenees and some other montane districts of northern Spain, in moist and shady places on mountain rocks and in pastures at 1,000-2,300 m.

It is generally scarce as a garden escape in Britain and Ireland except for parts of north-east Scotland.

Cultivated from 1776, it was first found in the wild in 1878 (Preston *et al.*, 2002).

V. cornuta *showing the large, serrated stipules.*

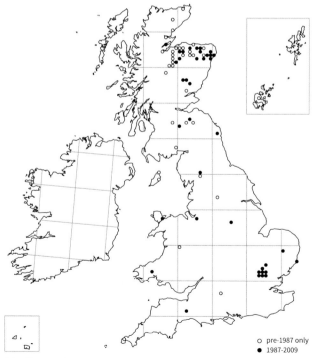

O pre-1987 only
● 1987-2009

Distribution of V. cornuta.

Rear view of the white form of V. cornuta *showing the long, slightly curved spurs and the large sepal appendages.*

Notes

Cultivars – Some commercial growers split *V. cornuta* into three groups based on colour, namely Purpurea, Lilacina and Alba, but other colours and varieties are now available and these too may well escape into the wild.

Flowering – In its native habitat *V. cornuta* flowers during June and July but its cultivated forms have a much longer flowering season, starting earlier and continuing, though less profusely, throughout the summer and into the autumn if the season is mild. Cutting back during summer is often recommended so as to produce a late flush of flowers in late summer and autumn.

Infraspecific taxa and hybrids

No infraspecific taxa or natural hybrids are recorded although the hybrid between *V. cornuta* and *V.* × *wittrockiana* has been commercially cultivated for garden bedding plants (*V.* × *williamsii*) and these may sometimes escape into the wild. Often known as bedding Violas, they are described as having the perennial nature and tufted habit of *V. cornuta* with the large rounded flowers of *V.* × *wittrockiana* but lacking the mask or face pattern (The Alpine Garden Society, 2011).

Mountain Pansy

Viola lutea is especially characterised by its compact habit and usually single, disproportionately large, yellow, yellow-blue, or blue flowers.

A perennial herb producing slender rhizomes which can become mat-forming. **Petioles** usually simple, solitary, to 20 cm. **Stipules** subpalmately divided into several ± linear lobes; terminal lobe linear-oblanceolate, entire, to 2 mm wide. **Leaves**, lower ovate, bluntly-toothed, becoming progressively narrower above; uppermost to 2 cm long, oblong-lanceolate with a cuneate base, crenate; with short hairs on margins and veins. **Pedicels** to 9 cm; normally 1-2 per stem. **Bracteoles** in upper half of pedicel. **Sepals** triangular-lanceolate, acute; appendages dentate. **Flowers** yellow, blue, purple, or a combination of these colours but invariably yellow at the base of lower petal; corollas large (1.5-)2.0-3.5 cm measured vertically; ± flat; the three lower petals with darker veins. **Spurs** 3-6 mm long; 2-3 ×

V. lutea, *yellow form, showing the large, single flowers.*

Viola lutea.

length of sepal appendages. **Capsules** ovoid, small; seeds ellipsoid
1.5 × 0.5 mm. **Flowering** late April to September. **Chromosome
number** 2n = 48.

In Britain and Ireland the distribution of *V. lutea* is restricted by climatic
and edaphic factors. It is mostly confined to the north and west of
Britain, with scattered occurrences in eastern and western Ireland
and on the western isles of Scotland but is absent from Orkney and
Shetland. It is frequent in the upland areas of Wales and the Derbyshire
Peak District. Northward of here there is a short break until the Craven
limestone area of Yorkshire is reached where it is also frequent.
Thereafter it occurs almost continuously through much of the
upland areas of the Pennines, the Lake District and through Scotland
northwards to the Great Glen. In western Ireland it is found at sea-level
but elsewhere not usually below 200 m but it ascends to almost 1,100
m in central Scotland. In mainland Europe *V. lutea* is known from
France and Belgium then eastwards through much of central Europe.

V. lutea is mainly a plant of unimproved grassland and stony areas
in mountain pastures, on slightly acidic to base-rich substrates. It
can also occur in large populations in the short turf on spoil heaps

V. lutea, *showing the dentate
sepal appendages, the spur
which comfortably exceeds
them and the bracteoles near
the top of the pedicel. Photo:
J.R. Crellin.*

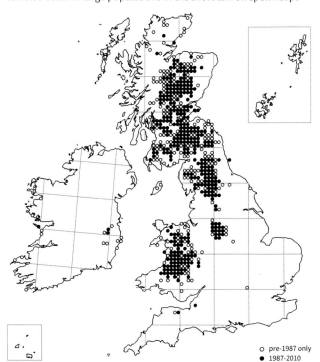

○ pre-1987 only
● 1987-2010

Distribution of V. lutea.

106

Leaf of V. lutea *showing the short hairs along the edge and on the veins.*
Photo: J.R. Crellin.

of disused lead mines and over other heavy-metal substrates. In
limestone districts, where it is perhaps at its most frequent, it prefers
soils from which much of the calcium carbonate has been leached
and which have become neutral to mildly acidic. It can also occur on
igneous formations as in the Northumberland Cheviots.

The conservation status in Britain is Least Concern (Cheffings & Farrell,
2005) but is Near Threatened in England (Stroh *et al.*, 2014). In Ireland
it is, provisionally, classed as Vulnerable (M.B. Wyse Jackson, pers.
comm, 2015). The vegetation in which *V. lutea* occurs is normally
maintained either by grazing, hay-making, or by periodic disturbance
such as flooding. Accordingly, *V. lutea* is fairly resistant to grazing and
in closely-grazed areas it is usually a small, compact plant with the
flowers prominent but the leaves and stipules partially concealed close
to the turf. Where competition is greater, it can become much larger
and shrubby. A relaxation of grazing intensity has been associated
with increased flowering in some of the populations studied. It is also
resistant to cold and to snow cover. Although still widespread, *V. lutea*
has declined in Britain in the past 25 years. This is most likely related to
changes in agricultural and land management methods. Historically,
liming was a common agricultural practice in marginal upland areas
and soils have probably become progressively more acidic as this
practice has ceased, leading to a decline in *V. lutea* populations. It
is not resistant to drought, disturbance such as ploughing, or the
application of fertiliser and will take a considerable time to re-establish
after such conditions.

Various colour forms of V. lutea. *Note that even the flowers which are almost wholly purple or blue have some yellow at the base of the lowest petal.*

V. lutea is associated with several NVC communities, covering a range of acid, neutral and calcareous grasslands. These include **U4** *Festuca ovina-Agrostis capillaris-Galium saxatile* grassland in northern and western Britain; **MG3** *Anthoxanthum odoratum-Geranium sylvaticum* grassland in northern England and Scotland, characteristic of upland hay meadows; **CG12** *Festuca ovina-Alchemilla alpina-Silene acaulis* dwarf herb community in montane Scotland, especially characteristic of the calcareous mica-schist of Ben Lawers; and **OV37** *Festuca ovina-Minuartia verna* community on heavy-metal contaminated substrates in northern and western Britain (Rodwell, 1991-2000).

Associated species include *Agrostis capillaris*, *Anthoxanthum odoratum*, *Armeria maritima*, *Botrichium lunaria*, *Cynosurus cristatus*, *Festuca ovina*, *Galium saxatile*, *Hieracium pilosella*, *Minuartia verna*, *Ophioglossum vulgare*, *Pimpinella saxifraga*, *Polygala serpyllifolia*, *Potentilla erecta* and *Veronica officinalis*.

Probably the first British record for *V. lutea* was that given in John Gerard's *Herbal* where it was said to have been found by Thomas Hesketh 'upon the hils in Lancashire, neere unto a village called

Latham' (Gerard, 1597) and this record is repeated by Merrett (1666) as '*Viola martia lutea*'. The site is very probably (sand) hills at Lytham St Annes, Lancashire (v.c. 60 W. Lancs.). Towards the end of the seventeenth century, the pioneering Cumbrian Quaker botanist, Thomas Lawson, also found it to be abundant on the moors of Stainmore on the border of Cumbria and north Yorkshire (v.c. 65 N. W. Yorks./v.c. 69 Westmorland).

Notes

Irish population – In the Burren area of western Ireland, *V. lutea* is recorded from coastal sand dunes. This is a most unusual habitat and there has been speculation that these yellow-flowered plants may be transitional to *V. tricolor* subsp. *curtisii*. However, they are much larger-flowered and, following a recent examination of herbarium material collected from here, it was found difficult to refer the plants to anything other than *V. lutea*. An elucidation of their taxonomic status through molecular means would be instructive.

Pollination – *V. lutea* reproduces both vegetatively and by seed and is thought to have a persistent soil seedbank. Seeding is from late June onwards, with germination the following February. There is no record of cleistogamy. Pollination appears to be mainly carried out by bees but other (dipterous) insects such as *Hylemyia lasciva*, *Siphona geniculata* and *Anthomyia* sp., have also been recorded.

Infections – The fungal rust *Pucciniade pauperans* is frequently reported as being present on *V. lutea*.

Infraspecific taxa and hybrids

- var. *hamulata* Baker (see **11 × 14**)
- var. *amoena* Henslow
- hybridises with *V. tricolor* (see **11 × 12**)
- hybridises (probably) with *V. arvensis* (see **11 × 14**)
- artificially hybridised with *V. tricolor* and (?) *V. altaica* to form
  V. × wittrockiana (see **13**)

V. lutea populations in which the flowers are almost entirely purple-blue have been referred to var. *amoena* Henslow. These plants appear to occur in the more northerly parts of the British range but are probably no more than a mere colour form (or it is possible that some might have been the hybrid with *V. tricolor*).

The British and Irish plants are subsp. *lutea*. However, in mainland Europe the subsp. *sudetica* (Willd.) W. Becker occurs in mountains beyond 14 deg. east and in Czechoslovakia it hybridises with *V. tricolor* (Krahulcová *et al.* 1996). This subspecies is a more robust plant than subsp. *lutea* with the leaves and stipules glabrous or nearly so, the upper leaves lanceolate to 4 cm long, and with much wider stipule segments. Two other subspecies (or varieties) are represented by populations of a threatened, clonal plant, generally referred to as 'subsp. *calaminaria*', which is endemic to sites in eastern Belgium, Holland and Germany; it possesses a high calamine (zinc mineral) content. Such plants are considered mostly allogamous in comparison to subsp. *lutea* and have a higher chromosome number (2n = 52) and were first described at specific level by Lejeune (1811). They are mainly yellow-flowered but a blue-flowered population at Blankenrode, Germany, has been considered to be taxonomically distinct. However, following recent phylogenetic work by Hildebrandt *et al.* (2006) the authors classified these as *V. lutea* subsp. *westfalica* and subsp. *caliminaria*, respectively. More recently, Bizoux & Mahy (2007) have reported further on such plants.

Corolla of V. lutea *var.* amoena.

Viola lutea hybrids

In 1863, J.G. Baker gave a detailed account (Baker, 1863) of an unusual *Viola* which he had collected from two localities in North Yorkshire (Richmond Racecourse and Reeth) and to which he applied the name *Viola lutea* var. *hamulata* [= sickle-shaped]. This plant has an interesting history. Baker considered it to be a 'curious plant....with small yellow flowers, petals standing forward as in the cornfield *V. arvensis* and stipules with sickle-shaped lateral and crenate leafy terminal lobes'. In 1864, a fire at Baker's home in Thirsk destroyed virtually all his property including his botanical manuscript notes and herbarium and his specimens of var. *hamulata* were thought to have met the same fate. Much later, his son Edmund Gilbert Baker believed his father's site at Reeth to be the lead mines on Copperthwaite Moor [Marrick Moor]. Fortunately, specimens from here collected by Baker in 1863 survive in at least two herbaria (**BM** & **LIV**) but over the past hundred and fifty years or so, this plant seems to have been totally forgotten. Searches on Marrick Moor (v.c. 65 N. W. Yorks.) in June 2006 led to the discovery of a large population of what is almost certainly Baker's plant and a close examination suggested the possibility of it being of hybrid origin (see **11 × 14**).

In Britain and Ireland, the only wild population of *Viola lutea × tricolor* which has been unequivocally confirmed was the large one studied by Fothergill at Bywell, Northumberland on the banks of the River Tyne (v.c. 67 S. Northumb.). This population now appears to be extinct. Fothergill (1938, 1939, 1941) examined these plants closely and synthesised the hybrid artificially, finding that, in morphology, the latter compared very closely to the Bywell plants. He found, in most cases, the hybrid to either possess a majority of *V. lutea* characters or to be more or less intermediate between the parents. Plants possessing a preponderance of *V. tricolor* characters were infrequent. He also found the hybrid to be characterised by increased vigour and size of parts and, especially, in its possession of enlarged stipules with a broadened base and with the lateral lobes of the stipule positioned higher above their base. This latter confirmed the conclusions of Drabble (1909) who first observed this character in putative *Viola* hybrids.

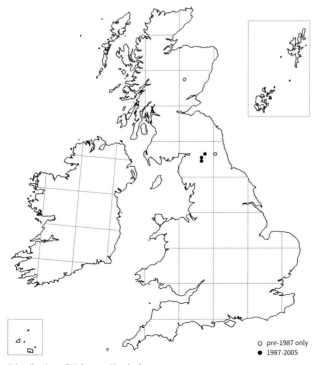

○ pre-1987 only
● 1987-2005

Distribution of V. lutea × V. tricolor.

Putative V. lutea × tricolor *from Williamston, Northumberland, showing intermediate habit and large flowers.*

In addition, the hybrid can be distinguished from *V. lutea* by its larger size, its rather lax and more branched habit and by its multi-coloured flowers. However, true plants of *V. lutea* can also possess flowers of such a colour and are sometimes misidentified as the hybrid. From *V. tricolor* it also differs in its less elongated, spreading habit and its larger often more vividly coloured flowers. Chromosome numbers in the range 2n = 46-52 have been measured and compare to *Viola lutea* 2n = 48, 50 and *V. tricolor* 2n = 26. Clausen (1931) also produced artificial hybrids via *V. 'tricolor hortensis'* and with *V. 'tricolor alba'* as female parents. Meiosis was very irregular, with mostly 8-11 bivalents. The fertility of the F1 was poor although plants were raised as far as the F4 generation.

Most of the relatively few existing records for this hybrid in Britain and Ireland are considered suspect, especially those from Derbyshire (v.c. 57 Derbys.) given by Valentine (1975). These have not been substantiated and no specimens confirmed by him have been traced.

Viola lutea × tricolor.

The hybrid has also been recorded from Glen Isla, Angus (v.c. 90 Angus). Probably the main cause of its rarity is that the parents are of strikingly different habitats, *V. lutea* being decidedly upland whereas *V. tricolor* is lowland and arable/ruderal. Despite this, the hybrid is likely to be under-recorded and herbarium material examined suggests its one-time occurrence elsewhere. Based on Fothergill's findings and an examination of preserved specimens from the extinct Bywell population held at the University of Newcastle, populations occurring elsewhere on the banks of the Tyne and its tributaries, as well as other rivers in northern England, have recently been determined as containing the putative hybrid. It also occurs in France and the Czech Republic, in the latter as a subspecies of *V. lutea* (Krahulcová *et al.* 1996).

Putative Corolla of V. lutea × tricolor *from Williamston, Northumberland, showing diverging upper petals.*

Scan of some of the original specimens of V. lutea × tricolor *collected from classic site on the Tyne at Bywell by Fothergill.*

Note

Origin – On the River Tyne, this hybrid appears to have originated as a result of plants of *V. lutea* being washed downstream from near the headwaters and coming in contact with the lowland, more ruderal,

V. tricolor. In this upland area, *V. lutea* is frequent on the lead- and zinc-rich metaliferous soils which were mined commercially in the eighteenth and nineteenth centuries. Part of the mining process was known as 'hushing' whereby extracted earth-containing ore (and therefore any accompanying *Viola* plants) were placed in dammed tributary streams. The waters were then released in order to wash earth from the ore. This resulted in an accumulation of heavy-metal gravels in the river water so that when in flood, metal-contaminated alluvium was washed downstream and deposited at the margins of the slower moving reaches. As these deposits consolidated, the accompanying *Viola* plants became established in this sparsely-populated, specialised habitat. Hybridisation with the nearby arable/ruderal, lowland *V. tricolor* then appears to have been only a short step away.

Viola lutea	*Viola lutea* × *tricolor*	*Viola tricolor*
Habitat usually upland, often on substrates with a heavy-metal content.	Habitat on, or close to, heavy-metal substrates, especially by river margins.	Habitat lowland, often ruderal.
Plants relatively small, compact, with a largely unbranched habit.	Plants intermediate in size, habit relatively lax, sometimes branched, exhibiting increased vigour and size of parts compared to *V. lutea*.	Plants relatively large, branched, habit distinctly lax.
Stipules not enlarged or especially broad based; lateral lobes not positioned high above the base.	Stipules enlarged with a broadened base; lateral lobes positioned high above the base.	Stipules not enlarged or especially broad based; lateral lobes not positioned high above the base.
Lower leaves ± rounded.	Lower leaves ± rounded.	Lower leaves ovate-lanceolate.
Corollas relatively large compared to size of plant, *c.* 20-35 mm vertically, upper petals not diverging.	Corollas relatively large compared to size of plant, *c.* 20-25(30) mm vertically, upper petals diverging.	Corollas not relatively large compared to size of plant, *c.* 18-22 mm vertically.
Corollas yellow, blue, blue-purple, or a combination of these colours.	Corollas varied in colour, often multi-coloured, blue, yellow and purple, or a mixture of these (but more purple-blue than the bright sky blue of *V. tricolor*).	Corollas mainly sky blue or darker, sometimes with pale, almost white, lower petals, the lowest with an orange-yellow centre.

A putative hybrid

The hybrid *Viola lutea × arvensis* has never been conclusively confirmed in Britain or Ireland. However, recent field work has suggested that a large population occurring on Marrick Moor near Hurst in Yorkshire (v.c. 65 N. W. Yorks.) and some small populations at Smailholm Tower in Roxburghshire (v.c. 80 Roxburghs.) and Hareheugh Craigs in Berwickshire (v.c. 81 Berwicks.) may be of this parentage. At these localities, plants appear to be morphologically identical and exhibit little variation within their respective populations and possess characters of both putative parents.

From *V. lutea,* these plants differ in having much smaller flowers, the upper petals almost pure white, the lateral tinged yellow, and the lower a clear yellow. From *V. arvensis* they differ in their larger, less cup-shaped flowers and their less leafy, less robust habit. At both localities typical *V. lutea* is present, usually in small, discrete groups whilst *V. arvensis* occurs in close proximity at one locality and is suspected

Corollas of two putative specimens of Viola lutea × arvensis, *the top one from Hareheugh Craigs, Berwickshire and the bottom one from Marrick Moor, North Yorkshire.*

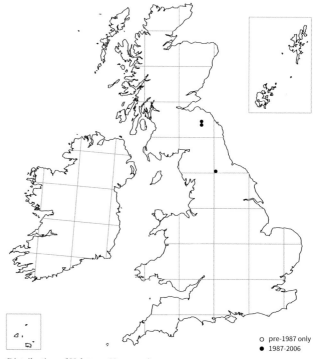

○ pre-1987 only
● 1987-2006

Distribution of V. lutea × V. arvensis.

as being present in nearby cultivations at the other. The Yorkshire population is thought to be the same as that described as *V. lutea* var. *hamulata* Baker (Baker, 1863; Foley & Porter, 2007) (see **11**) and is at least partially fertile. To establish the hybrid status (or otherwise) of these plants, a genetic evaluation together with a chromosome count will be required. *Viola lutea* 2n = 48, 50; *V. arvensis* 2n = 34.

Note

Unpublished experimental work carried out at Kew involving the cultivation of the hybrid between *V. lutea* and *V. arvensis* produced plants of very similar appearance to the putative hybrid described above (R.D. Meikle, pers. comm).

Putative Viola lutea × arvensis, *growing near Hurst on Marrick Moor, North Yorkshire, probably the same site as that found by Baker in the mid-nineteenth century.*

Viola lutea	Putative hybrid	Viola arvensis
Habitat usually upland, often on substrates with a heavy-metal content.	Habitat similar to *V. lutea* and growing in association with it but in clearly separable distinct populations. Known from north Yorkshire as *V. lutea* var. *hamulata*, and the Scottish Borders (two populations).	Habitat lowland, almost entirely ruderal.
Plants small, with a neat compact habit, usually unbranched.	Plants very small, habit neat and very compact, unbranched.	Plants relatively large, habit often much-branched, not neat, shrubby.
Corollas relatively large, *c.* 20-35 mm, vertically; ± flat.	Corollas small, delicate, 12-14 mm vertically; ± flat.	Corollas relatively small, *c.* 10-12 mm vertically; cup shaped.
Corollas yellow, blue, blue-purple, or a combination of these colours, yellow at the base of the lowest petal.	Corollas usually yellow and white, but some with an admixture of blue.	Corollas all cream (except the lowest having an orange-yellow centre).

Wild Pansy, Heartsease

Viola tricolor is very variable, but is probably best characterised by its branched habit with several flowers per stem, its corollas ± flat, the petals in a combination of sky blue, violet, yellow and cream, and the upper petals 1.5-2 × the length of the upper sepals.

A very variable, glabrous to pubescent, branched, annual or perennial herb with a compact to lax sprawling habit; usually lacking creeping rhizomes. **Petioles** hairy; to 20 mm. **Stipules** palmately-lobed to midrib; midlobe narrowly elliptic to oblanceolate, slightly crenate to entire. **Leaves** variable; lower oval-ovate, obtuse, becoming narrower above; upper oblong-lanceolate to elliptic, margins crenate; apex obtuse to subacute; base cuneate; glabrous or pubescent. **Pedicels** to 8 cm; pedicel arch not especially grey-blue. **Sepals** sub triangular to linear-lanceolate, acute; variable appendages. **Flowers** several per stem; purple, sky blue, violet, yellow or cream, usually in a combination of these colours; corollas (1.0-)1.8-2.2(-2.5) cm vertically,

V. tricolor *showing the branched and rather straggly habit.*

Viola tricolor.

± flat, not cup-shaped; lowest petal usually orange-yellow towards centre; upper petals 1.5-2 × length of upper sepals. **Spurs** to 6 mm; up to 2 × length of sepal appendages. **Capsules** trigonous, 4-7.5 × 2-3 mm; glabrous. **Flowering** April to September. **Chromosome number** 2n = 26.

V. tricolor s.l. is widespread throughout Britain and Ireland in its many forms although less frequent in Ireland. The coastal ecotype is frequent on the dune systems of south and north Wales, Lancashire, Cumbria, and much of Scotland, especially the machair of the Outer Hebrides. It is also found around much of the coast of Ireland, although some populations on the west side have caused confusion and are thought possibly to be derived from *V. lutea* The true subsp. *curtisii* is of much more restricted distribution, occurring at the classic coastal site at Braunton Burrows in Devon (v.c. 4 N. Devon) where it was first found, and on some sandy acidic heaths in Breckland in East Anglia. It is possible that it might also occur locally in Ireland but more work is needed in order to confirm this. In Europe, *V. tricolor* s.l. occurs from Iceland and Scandinavia, southwards to the northern Mediterranean

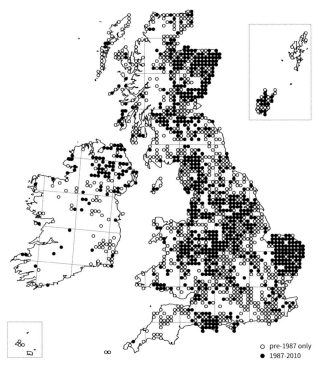

○ pre-1987 only
● 1987-2010

Distribution of V. tricolor.

Viola tricolor *coastal ecotype*.

V. tricolor. *note the sepals are totally concealed behind the petals and the lowest petal is orange-yellow towards the top.*

and eastwards through Turkey to the Urals and the Caucasus. It is also found in the mountains of north-west Africa and is naturalised in Asia, North America and Australia. The subsp. *curtisii* has also been tentatively recorded from the coast of the Baltic but it is possible that these populations are merely coastal ecotypes of subsp. *tricolor* (sometimes referred to as subsp. *maritima* (K.G. Hagen) Hyl.). If so, subsp. *curtisii* is endemic to Britain and Ireland. Detailed genetic work to establish the true identity of subsp. *curtisii* in relation to these widespread probable coastal ecotypes is urgently needed.

V. tricolor subsp. *tricolor* is mostly a plant of ruderal, waste areas, grazed acidic to neutral grassland, and arable field margins, the latter being a habitat in which it readily hybridises with *V. arvensis* and where it can cause confusion in identification. The true subsp. *curtisii* appears to be confined to a single sand dune system in south-west England and to sandy heaths in the East Anglian brecklands.

The conservation status of *V. tricolor* s.l. in Britain is Near Threatened (Cheffings & Farrell, 2005) and is the same in England (Stroh *et al.*, 2014). In Ireland it is, provisionally, classed as Least Concern (M.B. Wyse Jackson, pers. comm., 2015). Subsp. *tricolor* is Near Threatened in Britain and also in England whilst subsp. *curtisii* is Least Concern in Britain but Near Threatened in England.

NVC communities in which *V. tricolor* subsp. *tricolor* occurs include **OV1** *Viola arvensis-Aphanes microcarpa* community; **OV27** *Epilobium angustifolium* community; **SD7** *Ammophila arenaria-Festuca rubra* semi-fixed dune; **SD8** *Festuca rubra-Galium verum* fixed dune grassland; **SD11** *Carex arenaria-Cornicularia-aculeata* dune; and **SD19** *Phleum arenarium-Arenaria serpyllifolia* dune annual community. *V. tricolor* subsp. *curtisii* is noted in the floristic tables of **U1** *Festuca ovina-Agrostis capillaris-Rumex acetosella* grassland, sub-community *Erodium cicutarium-Teesdalia nudicaulis* which, on the sample distribution map, appears limited to the East Anglian breckland, and **SD19** *Phleum arenarium-Arenaria serpyllifolia* dune annual community which, on the sample distribution map, appears to include the Braunton Burrows area in Devonshire (Rodwell, 1991-2000).

As a result of the wide range of habitats which *V. tricolor* can occupy, a list of its associates is too large and varied to be of value.

The first reference to this species appears to have been made by William Turner (1548) under the name *Trinitatis herba* 'called in english two faces in a hoode or panses' that 'groweth ofte amonge the corne'. E. Forster (1834) in English Botany described how this had been found by William Curtis prior to 1790 on 'Braunton-boroughs in Devonshire' (v.c. 4 N. Devon) and that Curtis had introduced it into his garden under the name *V. littoralis*.

Note

Herbal use – *V. tricolor* has long been known under the colloquial name as the Heartsease pansy and has a history of medicinal usage. It is claimed to have expectorant properties and was once used for chest complaints, as well as for the treatment of asthma, skin diseases, and as a diuretic, whilst the flowers have been used to make a dye. The name 'pansy' is believed to originate from the French word pensée (= thought) and was used in Shakespeare's Hamlet when Ophelia states 'There's pansies, that's for thoughts'.

Infraspecific taxa and hybrids

- subsp. *tricolor*
- subsp. *curtisii* (E. Forst.) Syme
- hybridises with *V. lutea* (see **11 × 12**)
- hybridises with *V. arvensis* (*V.* × *contempta*) (see **12 × 14**)

V. tricolor hybridises readily with *V. arvensis* in ruderal habitats and also occasionally with *V. lutea* on those rare occasions where their distributions overlap.

Viola tricolor subspecies

The two distinct subspecies that are recognised are subsp. *tricolor*, often with relatively large flowers and long branched stems, and subsp. *curtisii*, a more compact, lower-growing plant, with shorter stems, branched at the base, usually with smaller yellow and white flowers with relatively long white upper petals and a rather longer spur. Flowering can occur over a long period from April to September, especially in subsp. *tricolor*.

This is an extremely variable taxon which is prone to hybridise as well as occur in several ecotypic forms dependent upon habitat. It is possible that the true *V. tricolor* as originally described by Linnaeus may no longer occur in Britain or Ireland. Plants from most of the maritime dune systems in the west of Britain and Ireland have been loosely, but erroneously we believe, referred to *V. tricolor* subsp. *curtisii* (E. Forster) Syme but in nearly all cases these are merely dwarfed coastal ecotypes of subsp. *tricolor*. Nevertheless, plants which appear intermediate between the two, or even close to subsp. *curtisii*, can

The coastal ecotype of V. tricolor.

occur there. However, plants of some *Viola* dune populations on the west coast of Ireland have characters suggestive of both *V. lutea* and of subsp. *curtisii* and it is possible that genetic material of *V. lutea* might be involved in these, in Braunton Burrows and Breckland plants and even in plants from other dune systems. Work to establish the true identity of these needs to be carried out.

Where *V. tricolor* subsp. *tricolor* and *V. lutea* cohabit, or did so at one time, their tendency to hybridise again leads to confusion in identification (see **11**). In addition, *V. tricolor* is thought to have been one of the parents in the hybrid origin of *V.* × *wittrockiana*, the large flowered 'Garden Pansy' which can escape and become naturalised in the wild.

V. tricolor *subsp.* curtisii *at Braunton Burrows. Photo: J.R. Crellin.*

V. tricolor *coastal ecotype from Sandscale Haws, Cumbria.*

Above and below: Colour variation in V. tricolor *from Hayton, Cumbria.*

Viola tricolor × *V. arvensis*

Viola × contempta is a highly fertile hybrid. The flowers are usually intermediate in size between the parents, not cup-shaped or only slightly so. The petals are usually cream, ± patent, the upper often tinged mauve or pale blue, the laterals and lower petals cream (orange-yellow towards the centre) or sometimes ± uniformly tinged blue. The upper petals and upper sepal are ± similar in length, the arch of the pedicel is indistinctly grey-blue, and the habit of plant and the internode length are variable. *V. × contempta* may occur in a form which is almost completely intermediate between the parents (fairly rare) or possess a form approaching one or other parent, the latter probably being a result of introgressive back-crossing. Other than variation in stature, *V. tricolor* appears to be much the more variable. Whether this is due to other causes or is a result of multiple introgression over a great number of generations is debatable but, on balance, is probably the latter. Because of the considerable variability

Two examples of V. × contempta, *both showing the upper sepal barely longer than the upper petals which are tinged mauve or blue, the orange-yellow towards the flower centre and the only slightly cup-shaped flowers. In the top example the lower petals are cream coloured, in the bottom, tinged with blue.*

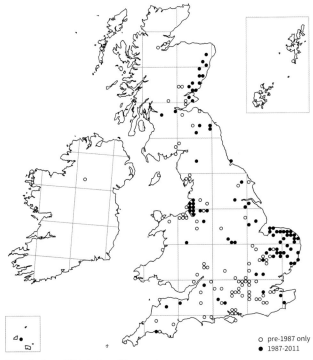

○ pre-1987 only
● 1987-2011

Distribution of V. tricolor × V. arvensis.

of the parents, particularly as regards habit, leaves and stipules, *V. × contempta* is best distinguished by its floral parts.

V. × contempta is scattered over most of Britain where the parents occur together. Where the parents do not frequently cohabit, such as in western Scotland and much of Ireland, there are few or no records. This may be accounted for in part by the difficulty of separating the hybrid from its parents. *V. × contempta* is found in central Europe and north to Scandinavia.

Pettet (1964) found the hybrid (and introgressed plants) to be quite common even in the absence of the *V. tricolor* parent and arrived at largely similar conclusions to the above. Putative F1 hybrids which he examined in a natural population were found to be morphologically indistinguishable from those he produced experimentally and were of the same intermediate chromosome number (2n = 30).

Both parents occupy ruderal habitats of low to moderate altitudes only and hence the hybrid is also found there. Waste ground, track sides and particularly the less disturbed margins of arable fields are especially favoured.

V. × contempta, showing the leafy habit, typical of both parents.

Viola tricolor	*Viola × contempta*	*Viola arvensis*
Corollas flat.	Corollas flat or slightly cup-shaped.	Corollas cup-shaped.
Upper petals greatly exceeding upper sepals.	Upper petals and upper sepals similar in length.	Upper sepals appreciably exceeding upper petals.
Corollas usually a combination of blue and yellow.	Corollas cream in colour or tinged blue.	Corollas cream or creamy-yellow but sometimes with a blue tinge.
Corollas usually 18-22 mm in size, measured vertically.	Corollas variably intermediate in size but usually closer to *V. arvensis*.	Corollas usually 8-12 mm in size, measured vertically.
Pedicel arch not especially grey-blue.	Pedicel arch indistinctly grey-blue.	Pedicel arch grey-blue.

Garden Pansy

Viola × *wittrockiana*
is characterised by its
often extremely large,
multicoloured flowers
with overlapping petals,
borne on long pedicels
and by its year round
flowering.

An annual cultivar. **Petioles** glabrous or slightly hairy; erect to
30 cm long. **Stipules** obovate, pinnatifid or palmate; midlobe large,
oblanceolate to obovate, obtuse; lateral lobes outward pointing.
Leaves ovate to lanceolate, to 50 × 20 mm, green; margin crenate to
serrate; base cuneate to slightly cordate. **Pedicels** to 10 cm. **Bracteoles**
in top half of pedicel; insignificant. **Sepals** lanceolate, 8-12 mm;
appendage 2-5 mm, *c.* 1/3 × length of sepals. **Flowers** arising from
upper part of stem; not fragrant; corollas large, to 6 × 6 cm, flat;
petals extremely varied in colour and patterning, often with obvious
dark veining; strongly overlapping at margins; upper petals to 4 × 4

V. × wittrockiana *in municipal flower pot, January.*

Viola × wittrockiana.

V. × wittrockiana *showing the overlapping petals and the dark veins.*

V. × wittrockiana *showing the large stipule with obovate midlobe.*

cm; lateral petals to 3 × 3.5 cm, upward- or outward-pointing; lower spurred petal to 2.5 × 3.5 cm. **Spurs** straight, to 7 mm long; violet; usually longer than sepal appendages. **Capsules** ovoid; very often not produced. **Flowering** of the different cultivars throughout the year. **Chromosome number** 2n = 48-50.

V. × wittrockiana occurs increasingly as an escape throughout lowland Britain, especially in the south, but is very rare in Scotland other than in the urbanised areas. In Ireland it is found in the south-east but is very scarce elsewhere. It is also found as an escape in many temperate regions of the world.

As a garden escape or throw-out, it occurs on tips, disturbed and waste ground, cultivated soil, roadsides and other ruderal areas, generally at low altitudes.

V. × wittrockiana was first recorded in the wild in 1927 (Preston *et al.*, 2002).

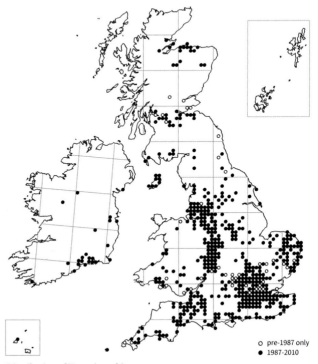

○ pre-1987 only
● 1987-2010

Distribution of V. × wittrockiana.

Infraspecific taxa and hybrids

The original *V. × wittrockiana*, the familiar Garden Pansy, was first cultivated in Britain in the early nineteenth century from hybrids between *V. lutea, V. tricolor* and *V. altaica* Ker-Gawler. Since then there have been many developments, involving further crosses with these species and with *V. cornuta*, and the name *V. × wittrockiana* is now used as an umbrella term for the resulting very large complex of variants (more than 800). Such plants differ greatly in flower size, flower colour and flowering times so the above description is based on characters common to most.

When occurring in the wild, all variants of the Garden Pansy may cross and introgress with native *Viola* species, particularly *V. tricolor*, to produce a puzzling range of plants with flowers often very much smaller than those of the Garden Pansy.

The garden hybrid, known as *V. × williamsii*, which has been bred by crossing *V. × wittrockiana* with *V. cornuta* produces plants which usually have smaller flowers than *V. × wittrockiana* (see **10**).

Field Pansy

Viola arvensis is characterised by its rather sprawling, shrubby habit, its small white to pale cream cup-shaped flowers, sometimes flushed blue, and the sepals appreciably exceeding the petals in length.

An annual herb, arising from a slender taproot. **Petioles** glabrous or hairy; erect or sprawling, to 40 cm; branched below. **Stipules** pinnatisect, lobed; midlobe leaf-like to 10-15 mm long; either elliptic to ovate, crenate or, occasionally, long, narrow, entire (probable introgression with *V. tricolor*). **Leaves** pale green, crenulate; base cuneate; lower elliptic to ovate, 20 × 13 mm; upper narrowly elliptic to 30 × 10 mm. **Pedicels** to 10 cm; pedicel arch characteristically coloured grey-blue. **Bracteoles** at or just below bend of pedicel. **Sepals** lanceolate, up to 2 × length of petals, appendages truncate, *c.* 0.3 × length of sepals. **Flowers** arising from aerial stems on pedicels; corollas variable in size, often small, 8-12(-20) mm vertically, usually ± cup-shaped; petals ± white to cream, sometimes tinged violet (probable introgression with *V. tricolor*); lowest petal grading to orange-yellow towards base. **Spurs** conical to cylindrical, straight; violet; *c.* 2 × length of sepal appendages. **Capsules** ovoid, trigonous, to 10 mm. **Flowering** continues over a long period from April to October. **Chromosome number** 2n = 34.

V. arvensis *showing the small, cup-shaped, pale flower and the rather shrubby habit.*

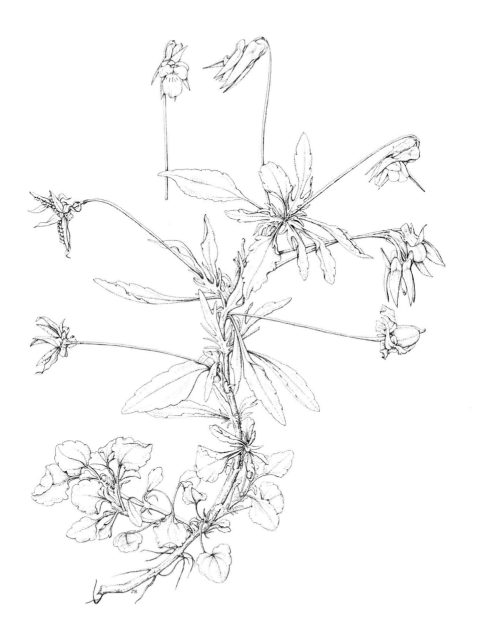

Viola arvensis.

V. arvensis. *the pale corolla much exceeded by the sepals.*

V. arvensis is widespread and common throughout England, Wales, the Channel Islands, the Isle of Man, and also in eastern Scotland as far north as the Moray Firth. It is much less frequent in the west and far north of Scotland and on the off-shore islands. In Ireland it is again frequent and widespread in the south-east but much scarcer towards the centre of the island and to the west and north. It is also native throughout most of Europe and Western Asia and is naturalised in Australasia, North America and, surprisingly, Greenland.

V. arvensis is especially a weed of open ruderal habitats, such as waste ground, road and track-sides, arable field margins, agricultural set-a-side, usually on neutral to basic substrates. Its associates are very wide-ranging, dependent on habitat.

The conservation status in Britain is Least Concern (Cheffings & Farrell, 2005) and is the same in England (Stroh *et al.*, 2014) and Ireland (M.B. Wyse Jackson, pers. comm., 2015). It is thought not to be under threat or in decline.

It occurs in the following NVC open habitat communities: **OV1** *Viola arvensis-Aphanes microcarpa*, **OV3** *Papaver rhoeas-Viola arvensis*,

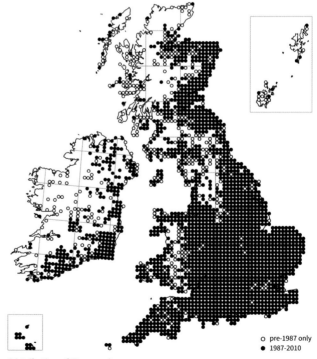

O pre-1987 only
● 1987-2010

Distribution of V. arvensis.

OV4 *Chrysanthemum segetum-Spergula arvensis* **OV5** *Digitaria ischmaemum-Erodium cicutarium*, **OV6** *Cerastium glomeratum-Fumaria muralis* ssp. *boraei*, **OV7** *Veronica persica-Veronica polita*, **OV9** *Matricaria perforate-Stellaria media*, **OV10** *Poa annua-Senecio vulgaris*, **OV11** *Poa annua-Stachys arvensis* **OV12** *Poa annua-Myosotis arvensis*, **OV16** *Papaver rhoeas-Silene noctiflora*, **OV21** *Poa annua-Plantago major*, **OV33** *Polygonum lapathifolium-Poa annua*, **OV36** *Lythrum hyssopifolia-Juncus bufonius* (Rodwell, 1999-2010).

V. tricolor is often an associate in arable field margins where the two frequently hybridise.

V. arvensis appears to have been the wild pansy referred to by John Gerard with 'the flowers [that] are a bleake and pale colour farre inferior in beautie to that of the garden' (Gerard, 1597).

V. arvensis. *showing the large sepal appendages and the grey-blue arch of the pedicel.*

Notes

Habit comparison – In comparison to *V. tricolor* with which *V. arvensis* often grows, its habit is denser, more leafy in the upper part, and with comparatively shorter internodes.

Introgression – Plants of apparently 'good' *V. arvensis* may sometimes exhibit single characters of *V. tricolor*, probably the result of past introgression.

Infraspecific taxa and hybrids

- possibly hybridizes with *V. lutea* (see **11 × 14**)
- hybridises with *V. tricolor* (*V. × contempta*) (see **12 × 14**)

V. arvensis readily hybridises with *V. tricolor* and in some cases the progeny can be difficult to separate from either one or other of the parents. In difficult cases their identities might be resolved by determining the average number of pollen grains present.

It is possible that *V. arvensis* also hybridises with *V. lutea* although this has never been conclusively confirmed in Britain or Ireland. However, recent field work suggests that a large population occurring near Hurst in north Yorkshire (v.c. 65 N. W. Yorks.) and two small populations in Roxburghshire (Scottish Borders) (v.c. 80 Roxburghs.) may be of this parentage (see **11 × 14**). At these localities the plants appear to be morphologically identical and exhibit little variation within their respective population and possess characters of both putative parents.

Dwarf Pansy

Viola kitaibeliana is characterised by its very small size, its usually unbranched habit, and its very small pale flowers, the corollas being concave and *c.* 5 mm vertically.

An annual herb with erect to decumbent stems, arising from a single taproot, 3-10 cm long; sometimes slightly branched; ± grey-pubescent overall. **Stipules**, lower bearing large ovate-lanceolate, serrate leaf-like midlobe but with a few lateral lobes; similar to but smaller than those of *V. arvensis*, 0.5-1.0 cm. **Leaves**, lowest sub-orbicular, obtuse; upper oblong-lanceoate, subacute, serrate, to 2 cm long. **Pedicels** exceeding leaves, 1-2(-4) cm; glabrous; deflexed at apex. **Bracteoles** two near base of curve; minute. **Sepals** subulate to oblong-lanceolate, *c.* 5 mm; glabrous; equalling or exceeding petals to varying degrees. **Flowers** arising from leaf axils; single, chasmogamous; cream-white to yellow or pale blue-violet; corollas very small, *c.* 5 mm high, ± concave; lower petal yellowish near the base; lateral petals 'bearded'. **Spurs** 1-2 mm long, violet; slightly longer than the sepal appendages. **Capsules** globular, smooth, 1.6 × 1.2 mm; seed ovoid. **Flowering** end March to May. **Chromosome number** 2n = 48.

V. kitaibeliana, showing the cream-white petals and the spurs which are a little longer than the sepal appendages. Photo: D. Holyoak.

Viola kitaibeliana.

V. kitaibeliana is not known on the mainland of Britain or Ireland
but is limited to localities close to sea-level in the Channel Islands
(Guernsey, Lihou, Herm and Jersey) and the Isles of Scilly (Tresco,
Teän and Bryher). It is currently known only from nine tetrads (2 km
squares) overall. On the continent it occurs along the Atlantic coasts
as far north as the Pas-de-Calais and possibly even to Belgium and is
most frequent in maritime sands. It also occurs throughout south and
central Europe, and eastwards around the Mediterranean (including
Algeria) to Turkey, the Middle East and Ukraine, as well as in central
Europe. It is also known from North America but is probably an
introduction there.

In its British localities, *V. kitaibeliana* is a native of coastal dunes, wind-
blown sand, and short turf over sandy soil close to the sea, although
on Guernsey it has also been found over thin soils on granite cliffs. It
can also occur on arable ground. On the dunes it is found in disturbed
areas such as around rabbit holes and also close to paths. In closed
turf the plants are very small. Its British localities are usually relatively
drought and frost-free and therefore harsh climatic conditions do not
normally pose a threat. In the dunes and close-cropped turf plants

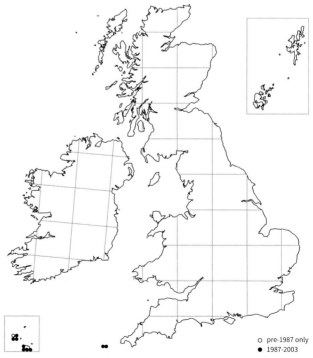

Distribution of V. kitaibeliana.

O pre-1987 only
● 1987-2003

V. kitaibeliana *showing a plant with a blue-violet flower. Photo: P.H. Oswald.*

Corolla of V. kitaibeliana *showing the sepals slightly exceeding the petals. Photo: Charles David. Provider: Guernsey Biological Records Centre.*

V. kitaibeliana *showing the pubescence on the leaves and petioles.*

*V. kitaibeliana on Jersey. The rabbit droppings give scale and show how small the plants and their flowers are.
V. kitaibeliana is often found close to rabbit holes. Photo: C. Gibson.*

dry up early and have usually disappeared by the end of May. Randall (2004) gives a detailed summary of the plant in Britain.

The conservation status in Britain is Near Threatened (Cheffings & Farrell, 2005) and is the same in England (Stroh *et al.*, 2014). It is a poor competitor and can be easily shaded out by encroaching vegetation. Correct management such as a restriction to light grazing only and mowing, where appropriate, are therefore most important for its success. In closed swards plants become depauperate although some protection from species such as *Carex arenaria* can be beneficial. It often occurs close to paths where trampling may be beneficial in helping to disperse seed. High levels of salinity are disadvantageous and plants tend to occur only several metres inland from the highest spring tides.

Ecological work on the Isles of Scilly (Coleman, 2005) found that *V. kitaibeliana* occurred in vegetation where winter annuals were frequent. This was different in character to the main NVC community **SD8** *Festuca rubra-Galium verum* fixed dune grassland community indicated by Randall (2004) but similar to the **SD19** *Phleum arenarium-*

Arenaria serpyllifolia community or to the **MC5c** *Armeria maritima-Cerastium diffusum-Aira praecox* sub-community (Rodwell, 1999-2010).

The first British record was made in the spring of 1871 from Jersey (v.c. 113(J) Channel Is (Jersey)) by Trimen who found it at St Aubyn's Bay (Trimen, 1871); subsequently a Miss Dawber recorded the plant at Grand Havre on Guernsey (v.c. 113(G) Channel Is (Guernsey)) in 1890 (Bennett, 1901). Meanwhile, in 1873, the plant had been found on Tresco in the Isles of Scilly (v.c. 1b Scilly) by J. Ralfs who considered it to be a variety of *V. curtisii*; a slightly later record from the Isles of Scilly is that of Curnow (1876).

Notes

Continental habitats – Whilst in Britain and much of western Europe it is a coastal plant, in central Europe it occurs inland in sandy areas, vineyards and arable fields. In Greece and Turkey it can occur at quite high altitudes and we have seen it on Chelmos in the Peloponnese flowering in June at 1,800 m in limestone scree.

Flowering – Flowering commences towards the end of March and continues during April and May before the plants quickly die back. However, in particularly moist or arable localities plants can continue to flower until early July.

Infraspecific taxa and hybrids

No infraspecific taxa are known in Britain but in the Iberian peninsula (Franco, 1971) two varieties have been recognised: var. *henriquesii* (Willk.) Beck and var. *machadina* (Cout.) Cout.

There is no definite record of hybridisation in Britain although on the Isles of Scilly a population occurred in the 1950s where plants bore flowers and fruits of *V. kitaibeliana* but had the habit and stipule characters of *V. arvensis*. In Turkey, the hybrid with *V. arvensis* has been suspected (Davis, 1965).

Glossary

The terms in this glossary are defined with specific reference to *Viola* species.

Acuminate – tapering gradually to a point.

Adpressed (or **appressed**) – of hairs; pressed close to leaf or stem.

Apiculate – with a small point at the apex.

Backcrossing – the crossing of a hybrid with one of its parents.

Bearded – with a tuft of hairs (on the lateral petals of most *Viola* flowers).

Bracteole – a tiny leaf-like structure on a flower stalk.

Capsule – a dry fruit holding the seeds.

Chasmogamous – of flowers that open fully.

Cleistogamous – of flowers that do not open and are self-pollinated.

Cordate – of leaf bases; heart-shaped, with a notch between two rounded lobes.

Corolla – the petals as a whole.

Crenate – of leaves; with blunt or rounded teeth, scalloped.

Crenulate – of leaves; minutely scalloped.

Cultivar – a plant variety produced in cultivation by selective breeding**.**

Cuneate – of leaf bases; wedge-shaped.

Decumbent – of stems; trailing on the ground and rising at the tip.

Decurrent – of leaves; where the base of the leaf continues along the petiole as a narrow wing.

Decurved – of spurs; curved downwards.

Deflexed – of stem hairs; bent sharply downwards.

Dentate – of sepal appendages; toothed.

Ecotype – a genetically and morphologically distinct geographic variety.

Fimbriate – of stipules; with a fringed margin.

Glabrous – of leaves or stems; hairless.

Glandular – of hairs; with a gland on the tip – under a lens looking like a tiny drop of liquid.

Hyaline – thin and translucent.

Indumentum – the hairy covering (of a leaf or stem) as a whole.

Internode – the portion of stem between two nodes.

Lanceolate – of leaves; long and narrow, gradually tapering to the tip.

Obovate – of leaves; with its broadest part above the middle.

Orbicular – of leaves; rounded, with length and breadth roughly the same.

Ovate – of leaves; egg-shaped in outline, broadest below the middle.

Palmate – of stipules; with 3 or more lobes arising from the same point.

Patent – of hairs on stem; projecting at right-angles.

    – of corolla petals; wide-open.

Pedicel – the stalk of a single flower.

Petiole – the stalk of a leaf.

Pinnatifid – of stipules; with several lobes, not cut as far as the midrib.

Pinnatisect – of stipules; with several lobes, cut almost to the midrib.

Pubescent – of leaves or stems; with short, soft hairs.

Recurved – of petals; bent or curved backwards or downwards.

Reniform – of leaves; kidney-shaped.

Reticulate – of leaves; with a distinct network of veins.

Rhizome – a perennial underground stem.

Saccate – of spurs; pouched or shaped like a sack.

Sepal – one of the outer whorl of green non-fertile parts behind the petals.

Sepal appendage – a small flap at the stem end of the sepal.

Serrate – of leaves; toothed like a saw.

Sobole – a creeping underground stem.

Spur – a hollow projection from the base of the lowest petal containing nectar.

Sterile – not producing fertile seeds or pollen.

Stipule – a leaf- or scale-like appendage at the base of a leaf; in pairs.

Stolon – a creeping stem or runner above ground.

Subulate – slender and tapering to a point.

Trigonous – of capsules; triangular.

Truncate – of leaf bases; cut off squarely.

References and selected bibliography

Articles and book titles in coloured text comprise the selected bibliography, not cited in the handbook, for further reading and information.

Aedo, C. & Lainz, M. (1991) Sobre la pretendida subsp. *juressi* (Link ex K. Wein) Coutinho de *Viola palustris* L. *Anales Jardin Botanico de Madrid* **49** 145-146.

Babington, C.C. (1863) *Viola arenaria*, De Cand., as a British plant. *Journal of Botany* **1** 325-326.

Baker, J.G. (1863) *North Yorkshire: studies of its botany, geology, climate, and physical geography*. London.

Balme, O.E. (1954) *Viola lutea* Huds. (Biological Flora of the British Isles) *Journal of Ecology* **42** 234-240.

Bennett. A. (1901) *Viola tricolor* L. var. *nana* DC. *Journal of Botany* **39** 72.

Bergdolt, E. (1932) Morphologische und physiologosche Untersuchungen über *Viola* zugleich ein Beitrag zur Lösung des Problems der Kleistogamie. *Botanische Abhandlungen und Beobachtungen* **20** 1-120.

Bizoux, J-P. & Mahy, G. (2007) Within-population genetic structure and clonal diversity of a threatened endemic metallophyte, *Viola calaminaria* (Violaceae). *American Journal of Botany* **94** 887-895.

Brewis, A., Bowman, P. & Rose, F. (1996) *The Flora of Hampshire*. Harley Books, Colchester.

Chater, A.O. (2010) *Flora of Cardiganshire*. A.O. Chater, Aberystwyth.

Cheffings, C.M. & Farrell, L. (eds), Dines, T.D., Jones, R.A., Leach, S.J., McKean, D.R., Pearman, D.A., Preston, C.D., Rumsey, F.J. & Taylor, I. (2005) The vascular plant red data list for Great Britain. *Species Status* **7**: 1-116. Joint Nature Conservation Committee, Peterborough.

Clapham, A.R., Tutin, T.G. & Warburg, E.F. (1962) *Flora of the British Isles*. 2nd ed. Cambridge University Press, Cambridge.

Clarke, W.A. (1900) *First records British flowering plants*. 2nd ed., p. 19. West, Newman & Co., London.

Clausen, J. (1931) Genetical and cytological investigations on Melanium violets. *Hereditas* **15** 219-308.

Coleman, C. (2005) Violets are blue…. *BSBI Recorder* Feb. 2005 (unpublished report).

Coombs, R.E. (2003) *Violets: The history and cultivation of scented violets*. 2nd ed. Batsford, London.

Corner, R.W.M. (1989) Observations on inland populations of *Viola canina* L. in south-eastern Scotland and north-western England. *Watsonia* **17** 351-352.

Culver, D.C. & Beattie, A.J. (1978) Myrmecochory in *Viola*: Dynamics of seed-ant interactions in some West Virginia species. *Journal of Ecology* **66** 53-72.

Curnow, W. (1876) A botanical trip to the Scilly Isles. *Hardwicke's Science Gossip*, 1876, 162.

Curtis, T.G.F. & McGough, H.M. (1988) *The Irish Red Data Book 1 Vascular Plants*. Stationery Office, Dublin.

Danihelka, J., van den Hof, K., Marcussen, T & Jonsell, B. (2010) *Viola montana* and *V. persicifolia* (Violaceae): Two names to be rejected. *Taxon* **59** 1867-1878.

Davis, P.H. (1965) *Flora of Turkey and the East Aegean Islands*. Vol. **1**. University Press, Edinburgh.

Drabble, E.(1909) The British Pansies. *Journal of Botany* **47** (2nd supplement) 1-32.

Druce, G.C. (1927) *The flora of Oxfordshire*. 2nd ed. Clarendon Press, Oxford.

Ferrez, Y. (2008) Note sur les violettes (*Viola* subgenus *Viola*) de Franche-Comté et du massif du Jura franco-suisse, proposition d'une clef de détermination pratique. *Les Nouvelles Archives de la Flore jurassienne* **6** 46-55.

Foley, M.J.Y. & Porter, M.S. (2007) Mountain Pansy (*Viola lutea* var. *hamulata* Baker) in N. Yorkshire (Exhibit). *BSBI News* **105** 47-48.

Forster, E. (1834) *Viola Curtisii*, Yellow sea pansy, tab. 2693. In: Hooker, W.J. *et al.* (1834) *Supplement to the English Botany…* Vol. **2**. London.

Fothergill, P.G. (1938) Studies in *Viola*. I. The cytology of a naturally occurring population of hybrids between *Viola tricolor* L. and *Viola lutea* Huds. *Genetica* **20** 159-186.

Fothergill, P.G. (1939) Studies in *Viola*. II. Some irregularities in natural *Viola* hybrids. *Genetica* **21** 153-176.

Fothergill, P.G. (1941) Studies in *Viola*. III. An account of the inheritance of certain characters in the progeny of a wild population of *Viola* hybrids. *New Phytologist* **40** 139-151.

Franco, J.do A. (1971) *Nova Flora de Portugal (Continente e Açores)*. Vol. **1**. Sociedade Astória, Lisbon.

French, C.N., Murphy, R.J. & Atkinson, M.G.C. (1999) *Flora of Cornwall*. Wheal Seton Press, Camborne.

Gerard, J. (1597) *The herball, or generall historie of plantes*. p. 701. J. Norton, London.

Gregory, E.S. (1912) *British violets. A monograph*. W. Heffer & Sons, Cambridge.

Grigson, G. (1955) *The Englishman's Flora*. Phoenix House, London.

Halliday, G. (1997) *A flora of Cumbria*. Centre for North-West Regional Studies, Lancaster.

Harmaja, H. (2003) A deviating cytotype of *Viola riviniana* from Finland. *Annales Botanici Fennici* **40** 395-400.

Hildebrandt, U., Hoef-Emden, K., Backhausen, S., Bothe, H., Bozek, M., Siuta, A. & Kuta, E. (2006) The rare, endemic zinc violets of Central Europe originate from *Viola lutea* Huds. *Plant Systematics and Evolution* **257** 205-222.

Info Flora Genève (2004-2015) www.infoflora.ch

Jalas, J. (1950) Zur Kausalanalyse der Verbreitumg einiger nordischen Os- und Sandpflanzen. *Annales Botanici Societatis Zoologicæ-Botanicæ Fennicæ 'Vanamo'* **24** 1-362.

Johnson, T. (1629) *Iter plantarum investigationis ergo susceptim a decem socii in agrum Cantianum …1629,* [A journey undertaken for the discovery of plants by ten fellows of the society into the county of Kent …1629, …]. (Printer unknown.)

Johnson, T. (1632) *Descriptio itineris plantarum investigationis ergo suscepti in agrum Cantianum 1632…* [The description of a journey undertaken for the discovery of plants in the county of Kent 1632…] T. Cotes, London.

Jonsell, B. & Karlsson, T. (eds) (2010) *Flora Nordica.* Vol. **6** *Thymelaeaceae to Apiaceae*. Swedish Museum of Natural History, Stockholm.

Jonsell, B., Nordal, I. & Roberts, J. (2000) *Viola rupestris* and its hybrids in Britain. *Watsonia* **23** 269-278.

Krahulcová, A., Krahulec, F. & Kirschner, J. (1996) Introgressive hybridization between a native and an introduced species: *Viola lutea* subsp. *sudetica* versus *V. tricolor*. *Folia Geobotanica Phytotaxonica* **31** 219-244.

Lejeune, A.L.S. (1811) *Flore des environs de Spa*. Vol. **1**. Liège.

Lousley, J.E. (1950) *Wild flowers of chalk and limestone*. Collins, London.

Mabey, R. (1996) *Flora Britannica*. Sinclair-Stevenson, London.

Marcussen, T., Nordal, I & Jonsell, B. (2001) Phytogeography in the *Viola rupestris* and *V. riviniana* complexes – a preliminary study. In: Stehlik, I., Tribsch, A. & Schönswetter (eds) (2001) Erstes gemeinsames Meeting zur Phylogeographie von arktischen und alpinen Pflanzen in Zürich, 1-3 June 2001, Abstracts der Beiträge. *Bauhinia* **15** 83.

Merrett, C. (1666) *Pinax rerum naturalium Britannicarum*. London.

Moore, D.M. (1957**)** *The experimental taxonomy of* Viola lactea *Sm.* Doctoral thesis, Durham University.

Moore, D.M. (1958) *Viola lactea* Sm. (Biological Flora of the British Isles) *Journal of Ecology* **46** 527-535.

Moore, D.M. (1959) Population Studies on *Viola lactea* Sm. and its wild hybrids. *Evolution* **13** 318-332.

More, A.G. (1861) *Viola Reichenbachiana*. *Report of Thirsk Natural History Society Botanical Exchange Club* **7**.

Mundell, T. (2013) Floral aberration in *Viola hirta*. *BSBI News* **122** 33.

Muñoz Garmendia, F. (ed.) (1993) Violaceae. In: *Flora Iberica*. Vol. **3**. Plumbaginaceae (partim) – Capparaceae. Consejo Superior de Investigaciones Científicas, Madrid.

Neuffer, B., Auge, H., Mesch, H, Amarell, U. & Brandl, R. (1999) Spread of violets in polluted pine forests: morphological and molecular evidence for the ecological importance of interspecific hybridization. *Molecular Ecology* **8** 365–377**.**

Nordal, I. & Jonsell, B. (1998) A phylogeographic analysis of *Viola rupestris*: three post-glacial immigration routes into the Nordic area? *Botanical Journal of the Linnean Society* **128** 105-122.

Nordal, I., Jonsell, B. & Marcussen, T. (2005) *Viola rupestris*: molecular analysis to elucidate postglacial migration in western Europe. *Journal of Biogeography* **32** 1453-1459.

Parkinson, J. (1640) *Theatrum Botanicum* p. 755. Thomas Cotes.

Partridge, J. (2007) *Viola × bavarica*: the punctual dog-violet? *BSBI News* **106** 8-9.

Pettet, A. (1964) Studies on British pansies. II. The status of some intermediates between *Viola tricolor* L. and *V. arvensis* Murr. *Watsonia* **6** 51-69.

Preston, C.D., Pearman, D.A. & Dines, T.D. (eds) (2002) *New atlas of the British and Irish flora*. Oxford University Press, Oxford.

Randall, R.E. (2004) *Viola kitaibeliana* Schult(es). *Biological Flora of the British Isles, No. 233. Journal of Ecology* **92** 361-369.

Ray, J. (1724) *Synopsis methodica stirpium Britannicarum*. 3rd ed., p. 364. London.

Rich, T.C.G. & Jermy, A.C. (1998) *Plant Crib* pp. 107-117. Botanical Society of Britain and Ireland, London.

Roberts, F.J. (1977) *Viola rupestris* Schmidt and *Juncus alpinus* Vill. In Mid-W. Yorkshire. *Watsonia* **11** 385-386.

Roberts, F.J. (2015) JRs Botanical Pages – Teesdale Violet *Viola rupestris*. www.edencroft2.demon.co.uk

Rodwell, J.S. (ed.) (1991-2000) *British Plant Communities*. Vols **1-5**. Cambridge.

Ross-Craig, S. (1950) *Drawings of British Plants*, Part **IV**. G. Bell & Sons, London.

Schmidt, A. (1961) Zytotaxonomische Untersuchungen an europäischen Viola-arten. *Österreichische botanische Zeitschrift* **108** 20-88.

Schöfer, G. (1954) Untersuchungen über die Polymorphie einheimischer Veilchen. *Planta* **43** 537-565.

Schultes, J.A. (1814) *Österreichs Flora. Ein Handbuch auf botanischen Excursionen,…* 2nd ed. vol. **1** p.426. Schaumberg, Vienna.

Smith, J.E. (1798) *Viola lactea*, Cream-coloured violet, tab. 445. In: Smith, J.E. (1798) *English Botany*. Vol. **7**. London.

Stace, C.A. (2010) *New flora of the British Isles*. 3rd ed. Cambridge University Press, Cambridge.

Stace, C.A. (ed.) (1975) *Hybridization and the flora of the British Isles*. Academic Press, London.

Stace, C.A., Preston, C.D. & Pearman, D.A. (2015) *Hybrid flora of the British Isles*. Botanical Society of Britain and Ireland, Bristol.

Stewart, A., Pearman, D.A. & Preston, C.D. (1994) *Scarce Plants in Britain*. Joint Nature Conservation Committee, Peterborough.

Stroh, P.A., Leach, S.J., August, T.A., Walker, K.J., Pearman, D.A., Rumsey, F.J., Harrower, C.A., Fay, M.F., Martin, J.P., Pankhurst, T., Preston, C.D. & Taylor, I. (2014) *A vascular plant red list for England*. Botanical Society of Britain and Ireland, Bristol.

The Alpine Garden Society (2011) http://encyclopaedia.alpinegardensociety.net/plants/Viola/williamsii

Tison, J-M. & de Foucault, B. (2014). *Flora Gallica – Flore complète de la France*. Société botanique de France.

Trees-Frick, I. (1993) Karyologische und morphologische Untersuchungen an *Viola reichenbachiana* Jord. ex Boreau und *Viola riviniana* Rchb. *Mitteilungen der Naturforschenden Gesellschaft in Bern. Neue Folge* **50** 81-98.

Trimen, H. (1871) Notes in Jersey and Guernsey. *Journal of Botany* **9** 198-201.

Turner, W. (1548) *The names of herbes…* John Day. London.

Tutin, T.G., Heywood, V.H., Burges, N.A., Moore, D.M., Valentine, D.H., Walters, S.M. & Webb, D.A. (eds) (1968) *Flora Europaea*. Vol. **2** Rosaceae to Umbelliferae. Cambridge University Press, Cambridge.

Valentine, D.H. & Harvey, M.J. (1961) *Viola rupestris* Schmidt in Britain. *Proceedings of the Botanical Society of the British Isles* **4** 129-135.

Valentine, D.H. (1941) Variation in *Viola Riviniana* Rchb. *New Phytologist* **40** 189-209.

Valentine, D.H. (1950) The experimental taxonomy of two species of *Viola*. *New Phytologist* **49** 193-212.

Valentine, D.H. (1956) Variation and Polymorphism in *Viola*. *Proceedings of the Royal Society of London*, Series B, *Biological Sciences*, **145**, No. 920 315-319.

Valentine, D.H. (1975) The taxonomic treatment of polymorphic variation. *Watsonia* **10** 385-390.

Valentine, D.H. (1975) *Viola* L. In: Stace, C.A. (ed.) (1975) *Hybridization and the flora of the British Isles*. Academic Press, London.

van den Hof, K., Danihelka, J., Marcussen, T., Jonsell, B., van den Berg, R.G. & Gravendeel, B. (2010) Proposals to reject the names *Viola montana* and *V. persicifolia* (Violaceae). *Taxon* **59** 1900-1902.

Walters, S.M. (1999) *Viola canina* L. ssp. *montana* (L.) Hartman (Violaceae). In: Wigginton, M.J. (ed.) (1999) *British red data books*. **1** *Vascular plants*. 3rd ed. p. 387. Joint Nature Conservation Committee, Peterborough.

Wigginton, M.J. (ed.) (1999) *British red data books*. **1** *Vascular plants*. 3rd ed. Joint Nature Conservation Committee, Peterborough.

Withering, W. (1796) *An arrangement of British plants…* 3rd ed. p. 262. Swinney, London.

Index

Names (including English names) accepted in this handbook are printed here in a non-italic typeface and referred to the taxon number (in **bold** face). Accepted subspecies are given letters after the species number in the index (e.g. **6a**) but NOT in the main text. Synonyms (including those not mentioned in the text but used by other authors) are in *italics* and are equated to a taxon by reference to its number. Those taxa otherwise mentioned in the text are referred to the page number of their main entry in light face.

altaica Ker-Gawler 131

arenaria DC .... **= 3**

arvensis Murray **14**

arvensis subsp. kitaibeliana (Schult.) Mateo & Figuerola .... **= 15**

× bavarica Schrank .... **4 × 5**

× burnatii Gremli .... **3 × 4**

calcarea (Bab.) Greg. 35

canina × lactea .... **6 × 7**

canina × stagnina .... **6 × 8**

canina L. **6**

canina subsp. *canina* × *stagnina* .... **= 6 × 8**

canina subsp. *canina* .... **= 6**

canina subsp. montana (L.) Hartm. **6a**

canina subsp. montana × stagnina .... **6a × 8**

canina subsp. ruppii (All.) Schübl. & G. Martens 74

canina var. crassifolia auct. **6**

canina var. *ericetorum* Rchb. .... **= 6**

Common Dog-violet **4**

× contempta Jord. .... **12 × 14**

cornuta L. **10**

curtisii E.Forst. .... **= 12a**

Dog-violet, Common **4**

Dog-violet, Early **5**

Dog-violet, Heath **6**

Dog-violet, Pale **7**

× *dubia* auct. .... **= 4 × 5**

Dwarf Pansy **15**

Early Dog-violet **5**

elatior Fr. 93

epipsila Ledeb. 98

ericetorum auct. .... **= 6**

Fen Violet **8**

Field Pansy **14**

flavicornis auct. .... **= 6**

Garden Pansy **13**

Hairy Violet **2**

Heartsease **12**

Heath Dog-violet **6**

hirta L. **2**

hirta subsp. calcarea (Bab.) E.F. Warb. 35

hirta var. calcarea Bab. 35

Horned Pansy **10**

× *intermedia* Rchb., non Krock. .... **= 4 × 5**

× intersita Beck .... **4 × 6**

juressi Wein **9a**

kitaibeliana Schult. **15**

kitaibeliana var. henriquesii (Willk.) Beck. 141

kitaibeliana var. machadina (Cout.) Cout. 141

labradorica Schrank 53

lactea Sm. **7**

lancifolia Thore .... **= 7**

littoralis Spreng. .... **= 12**

lutea × arvensis .... **11 × 14**

lutea × tricolor .... **11 × 12**

lutea Hudson **11**

lutea subsp. calaminaria (Ging.) Nauenb. 110

lutea subsp. lutea **11**

lutea subsp. sudetica (Willd.) W. Becker 110

lutea subsp. westfalica A.A.H. Schulz 110

lutea var. amoena Henslow 109

lutea var. hamulata Baker 110

Marsh Violet **9**

× militaris Savouré .... **6 × 7**

× mixta A. Kern. .... **5 × 6**

montana L. .... **= 6a**

Mountain Pansy **11**

nemoralis Kütz. .... **= 4**

odorata × hirta .... **1 × 2**

odorata f. lilacina Rossm. 25

odorata var. dumetorum (Jord.) Boreau 24

odorata var. imberbis (Leight.) Hensl. 24

odorata var. leucoium 25

odorata var. *odorata* .... **= 1**

odorata var. praecox Greg. 24

odorata var. subcarnea (Jord.) Parl. 25

odorata var. sulfurea (Cariot) Rouy & Foucaud 25

odorata var. *typica* .... **= 1**

odorata L. — 1
Pale Dog-violet — 7
palustris L. — 9
palustris subsp. juressi (Link ex Wein) Cout. — 9a
palustris subsp. palustris — 9
Pansy, Dwarf — 15
Pansy, Field — 14
Pansy, Garden — 13
Pansy, Horned — 10
Pansy, Mountain — 11
Pansy, Wild — 12
× permixta Jord. — 29
persicifolia Schreb. — = 8
pumila Chaix — 93
purpurea auct. — = 1
reichenbachiana × canina — 5 × 6
reichenbachiana Jord. ex Boreau — 5
reichenbachiana var. leucantha Beck — 66
× ritschliana W. Becker — 6 × 8
riviniana × canina — 4 × 6
riviniana × lactea — 4 × 7
riviniana × reichenbachiana — 4 × 5
riviniana f. luxurians auct. — 52
riviniana f. villosa auct. — 50
riviniana Rchb. — 4
riviniana var. minor (Murb. Ex Greg.) Valentine — 52
riviniana var. nemorosa Neuman, Wahlst & Murb. — 44
riviniana var. Purpurea group — 53
riviniana var. rosea auct. — 53
rubra auct. — = 9
rupestris × riviniana — 3 × 4
rupestris F.W Schmidt — 3
rupestris subsp. relicta Jalas — 41
rupestris subsp. rupestris var. glaberrima Murb. — 41
rupestris subsp. *rupestris* var. *rupestris* — = 3
rupestris subsp. *rupestris* — = 3
× scabra F. Braun — 1 × 2
× sepincola auct. — 29
silvestris auct. — = 5
stagnina Kit. ex Schult. — 8
Sweet Violet — 1
sylvatica auct. — = 4

sylvestris Lam. = **5**

Teesdale Violet **3**

tricolor L. **12**

tricolor subsp. arvensis (Murray) Gaudin = **14**

tricolor subsp. curtisii (E. Forst.) Syme **12a**

tricolor subsp. *maritima* (K.G. Hagen) Hyl. = **12a**

tricolor subsp. minima Gaudin = **15**

tricolor subsp. tricolor **12**

tricolor var. arvensis (Murray) Wahlenb. = **14**

tricolor var. arvensis DC = **14**

tricolor var. brevicalcarata Font Quer & Svent = **15**

tricolor var. kitaibeliana (Schult.) Ledeb. = **15**

tricolor var. *maritima* Schweigg. ex K.G. Hagen = **12a**

Violet, Fen **8**

Violet, Hairy **2**

Violet, Marsh **9**

Violet, Sweet **1**

Violet, Teesdale **3**

× *weinhartii* W. Becker = **4 × 6**

Wild Pansy **12**

× williamsii 131

× wittrockiana Gams ex Kappert **13**

The BSBI is for everyone interested in the flora of Great Britain and Ireland. Details of membership may be obtained from the Membership Secretary, Mr Gwynn Ellis, 41 Marlborough Road, Roath, Cardiff, CF23 5BU (E-mail gwynn.ellis@bsbi.org). The following books are available from the official agents for BSBI publications, Summerfield Books, Unit L, Skirsgill Business Park, Penrith, CA11 0FA (Tel. 01768 210793; E-mail info@summerfieldbooks.com). Fuller details can be found at www.summerfieldbooks.com under "BSBI Publications".

BSBI handbooks

Each handbook deals in depth with one or more difficult groups of British and Irish plants.

No. 1 **Sedges of the British Isles** – A. C. Jermy, D. A. Simpson, M. J. Y. Foley & M. S. Porter. Third edition, 2007, now incorporating full accounts of 35 species of Cyperaceae and 47 hybrids in addition to the 76 species and subspecies of *Carex*. 566 pp., including descriptions, line drawings and distribution maps. A5 paperback. [Previous editions 1968 and 1982.]

No. 2 **Umbellifers of the British Isles** – T. G. Tutin. 1980, reprinted 2006. 200 pp., with descriptions of 73 species facing line drawings by Ann Farrer. Small paperback.

No. 3 **Docks and Knotweeds of Britain and Ireland** – J. R. Akeroyd. 2014. 258 pp. Replaces *Docks and Knotweeds of the British Isles* by J. E. Lousley & D. H. Kent (1981). Descriptions of 83 species in 11 genera. All native and introduced but established species, as well as most casual species, are described, with new keys and distribution maps for many of the species. Drawings by Ann Farrer (some of them new). A5 paperback.

No. 4 **Willows and Poplars of Great Britain and Ireland** – R. D. Meikle. 1984, reprinted 2006. 200 pp., with descriptions of 65 species, subspecies, varieties and hybrids of *Salix* and *Populus*, illustrated with line drawings by Victoria Gordon. Small paperback.

No. 5 **Charophytes of Great Britain and Ireland** – Jenny A. Moore. 1986, reprinted 2005 and 2014 with a new preface and corrections by C. D. Preston. 144 pp., with descriptions of 39 species and varieties of Characeae (stoneworts), line drawings by Margaret Tebbs and 17 distribution maps. Small paperback.

No. 6 **Crucifers of Great Britain and Ireland** – T. C. G. Rich. 1991, reprinted 2006. 344 pp., with descriptions of 148 taxa of Brassicaceae (Cruciferae), 129 of them with line drawings by various artists, and 60 distribution maps. Small paperback.

No. 7 **Roses of Great Britain and Ireland** – G. G. Graham & A. L. Primavesi. 1993, reprinted with corrections 2005. 208 pp., with descriptions, facing line drawings by Margaret Gold, of 13 native and nine introduced taxa of *Rosa*, briefer descriptions of 76 hybrids, and 33 maps. A5 paperback.

No. 8 **Pondweeds of Great Britain and Ireland** – C. D. Preston. 1995, reprinted with minor alterations 2003 and 2015. 352 pp., with descriptions and line drawings of all 50 species and hybrids of *Potamogeton*, *Groenlandia* and *Ruppia*, most with distribution maps; detailed introductory material and bibliography. A5 paperback.

No. 9 **Dandelions of Great Britain and Ireland** – A. A. Dudman & A. J. Richards. 1997, reprinted with minor alterations 2000 and 2014. 344 pp., with descriptions of 235 species of *Taraxacum*, most of them illustrated by silhouettes of herbarium specimens; drawings of bud involucres of 139 species by Olga Stewart and 178 distribution maps. A5 paperback.

No. 10 **Sea Beans and Nickar Nuts** – E. Charles Nelson. 2000, reprinted 2003. 156 pp., with descriptions of nearly 60 exotic seeds and fruits found stranded on beaches in north-western Europe (many illustrated by Wendy Walsh) and of the mature plants (some with drawings by Alma Hathway), accounts of their history and folklore, growing instructions, etc. A5 paperback.

No. 11 **Water-starworts (*Callitriche*) of Europe** – R. V. Lansdown. 2008, reprinted 2015. 184 pp., with descriptions, line drawings by F. J. Rumsey and the author, and maps showing distribution in the British Isles and in Europe for all 16 *Callitriche* species and one hybrid reliably recorded in Europe; detailed introductory material, glossary and appendix listing the herbarium material studied. A5 paperback.

No. 12 **Fumitories of Britain and Ireland** – R. J. Murphy. 2009, reprinted 2015. 127 pp., with accounts of the ten British and Irish species and two casuals, including descriptions of any infraspecific taxa, line drawings, colour photographs, micrographs, keys, distribution maps, notes on hybrids and distribution of taxa by vice-county. A5 paperback.

No. 13 **Grasses of the British Isles** – Tom Cope & Alan Gray. 2009. 612 pp., with 182 full-page and some smaller line drawings by Margaret Tebbs. Keys to and descriptions of 15 tribes, 67 genera and 220 species (113 natives, 50 neophytes and 47 casuals); information on British and Irish distribution (with references to the *New Atlas* maps), habitats, biology and ecology, status and wider distribution. Published in association with the Centre for Ecology & Hydrology and the Royal Botanic Gardens, Kew. A5 softback with plastic cover and hardback.

No. 14 **Whitebeams, Rowans and Service Trees of Britain and Ireland** – Tim Rich, Libby Houston, Ashley Robertson & Michael Proctor. 2010. 223 pp., with descriptions of 52 native and naturalised *Sorbus* taxa in Britain and Ireland (44 species and eight hybrids). 43 of the taxa are native, 35 of them endemic to Great Britain and two to Ireland. 476 colour photographs, line drawings and maps. A4 hardback.

No. 15 **British Northern Hawkweeds** – Tim C. G. Rich & Walter Scott. 2011. 160 pp. A monograph of the 21 British species of *Hieracium* section *Alpestria*. Full accounts, line drawings, silhouettes of herbarium material, detailed photographs and general habitat shots. A4 hardback.

No. 16 **Evening-primroses (*Oenothera*) of Britain and Ireland** – R. J. Murphy. 2016. 96 pp., with accounts of the fourteen species and four hybrids found in Britain and Ireland, including descriptions of any infraspecific taxa, line drawings, colour photographs, keys, distribution maps and a glossary. A5 paperback.

Other BSBI publications

Alien Plants of the British Isles – E. J. Clement & M. C. Foster. 1994. 616 pp. A list of 3,586 recorded non-native species (of which 885 are established), with English names, frequency, status, origin, references to descriptions and illustrations, and selected synonyms. Paperback.

Alien Grasses of the British Isles – T. B. Ryves, E. J. Clement & M. C. Foster. 1996, reprinted with addenda 2008. 234 pp. A companion volume to the last, listing over 700 non-native grasses; includes keys to bamboos and eight of the larger and more difficult genera and 29 pp. of drawings by G. M. S. Easy. Paperback.

Illustrations of Alien Plants of the British Isles – E. J. Clement, D. P. J. Smith & I. R. Thirlwell. 2005. 480 pp., including 444 full-page line drawings of introduced, naturalised and casually occurring alien plants in Britain and Ireland. The drawings are largely from a collection put together by the late David McClintock, originally for publication in his planned Volume 3 of *A New Illustrated British Flora*. A5 paperback.

Plant Crib – T. C. G. Rich & A. C. Jermy. 1998, reprinted 2012 (with corrigenda included). 400 pp. An expertly written identification guide for some 325 difficult taxonomic groups, with explanations, keys and illustrations of plant details. A4 paperback.

List of Vascular Plants of the British Isles – D. H. Kent. 1992. 400 pp. Nomenclature and sequence as in Clive Stace's *New Flora of the British Isles* (1991, 1997), with selected synonyms. Paperback. Supplied with five errata lists. Three supplements (published 1996, 2000 and 2006) are also available.

Vice-county Census Catalogue of Vascular Plants of Great Britain, the Isle of Man and the Channel Islands – C. A. Stace, R. G. Ellis, D. H. Kent & D. J. McCosh (eds). 2003. 432 pp. A full listing by species of the vicecounties from which vascular plants have been recorded. A5 paperback.

Change in the British Flora 1987-2004 (A report on the BSBI Local Change survey) – M. E. Braithwaite, R. W. Ellis & C. D. Preston. 2006. 392 pp., with colour photographs, distribution maps, tables and graphs. A comparison of the results of two surveys of selected 2 km × 2 km squares. Large paperback.

50 Years of Mapping the British and Irish Flora 1962-2012 – Michael Braithwaite & Kevin Walker. 2012. 46 pp. A review of biological mapping since *Atlas of the British Flora* (1962), including mapping the flora at finer scales than the original hectad maps, aids to interpreting distribution maps and coincidence mapping. Illustrated throughout with colour photographs and maps. A5 paperback.

Atlas of British and Irish Brambles – A. Newton & R. D. Randall. 2004. 98 pp., with 330 hectad distribution maps of *Rubus* species, summaries of distribution and notes on changes. A5 paperback.

Atlas of British and Irish Hawkweeds – David McCosh & Tim Rich. 2011. 500 pp. Based on the account of 421 *Hieracium* and *Pilosella* species in Volume 4 of Sell & Murrell's *Flora of Great Britain and Ireland* (2006), each account has Latin and English names, hectad distribution map (with symbols for pre- and post-1960 records), representative silhouette, brief notes, list of vice-counties from which it has been recorded and IUCN threat category. Published in association with the National Museum of Wales. A5 paperback.

British Alpine Hawkweeds – David Tennant & Tim Rich. 2007. A monograph of British *Hieracium* section *Alpina*. 234 pp., with over 170 drawings and colour photographs and five paintings by Ramond C. Booth. All 39 taxa are described in detail, with their history, distribution maps, a gazetteer, habitats, ecology, biology, origins, cultivation, conservation status and details of relevant herbarium collections. A4 hardback and paperback.

A Vascular Plant Red List for England – P. A. Stroh *et al.* 2014. 192 pp. The first listing of England's vascular plant species measured against standardised IUCN criteria (with comments), preceded by 61 pages of introduction and explanation (with maps, figures, tables and colour photos). Published in association with the Centre for Ecology & Hydrology and Natural England. Large paperback.

Botanical Links in the Atlantic Arc – S. J. Leach, C. N. Page, Y. Peytoureau & M. N. Sandford (eds). 2006. 336 pp., with colour photograph section, black-and-white photographs, maps and figures. A wide-ranging series of papers on the flora of the atlantic coastal regions of Europe. Proceedings of an international conference held at Camborne, Cornwall, in 2003, published as BSBI Conference Report No. 24, dedicated to the memory of Dr Franklyn H. Perring. Hardback.

Current Taxonomic Research on the British and European Flora – J. P. Bailey & R. G. Ellis (eds). 2006. 156 pp., with colour photographs and text illustrations. Proceedings of a conference held at the University of Leicester in 2003 to mark the retirement of Prof. Clive Stace, published as BSBI Conference Report No. 25. Paperback.

Hybrid Flora of the British Isles – C.A. Stace, C.D. Preston & D.A. Pearman. 2015. 510pp., with distribution maps and text for 909 hybrids recorded in the Wild, with notes on another 156 further hybrids, which are either erroneous or which might possibly occur here. Some colour photographs.

Other publishers' books

Scarce Plants in Britain – A. Stewart, D. A. Pearman & C. D. Preston (eds). 1994. 518 pp. Accounts of the ecology, reproductive biology and British and world ranges of 254 nationally scarce taxa and of 71 formerly thought to be so, with updated distribution maps. Large hardback, published by JNCC. Out of print.

Aquatic Plants in Britain and Ireland – C. D. Preston & J. M. Croft. 1997. 365 pp. Accounts and distribution maps of 200 aquatic plants in 72 genera, with 72 line drawings by G. M. S. Easy. Large paperback edition, published by Harley Books in 2001 and reprinted by Brill in 2014.

New Atlas of the British & Irish Flora – C. D. Preston, D. A. Pearman & T. D. Dines (eds). 2002. 921 pp. Distribution maps and accompanying text for 2,412 plants, with introductory chapters. Very large hardback, with additional material on CD-ROM, published by Oxford University Press. Out of print, but *Online Atlas of the British & Irish Flora* (a joint project of the BSBI, Biological Records Centre and JNCC) can be accessed at www.brc.ac.uk/plantatlas/.

The Vegetative Key to the British Flora – John Poland & Eric Clement. 2009. 531 pp. (including numerous line drawings) and 26 full-page plates of colour photographs of leaves etc. Easy and rapid identification of nearly 3,000 native and alien plants without flowers or fruit, with nothing more than a hand lens; also selected floral and fruit characters, particularly ones not readily available in other Floras, especially in the comparatively few groups where they are essential; introduction, glossary and index. A5 softback, published by John Poland in association with the BSBI.